TOYS AND GAMES
for
EDUCATIONALLY
HANDICAPPED CHILDREN

TOYS AND GAMES
for
EDUCATIONALLY
HANDICAPPED CHILDREN

By

CHARLOTTE A. BUIST, R.N.

and

JEROME L. SCHULMAN, M.D.
Children's Memorial Hospital
Chicago, Illinois

CHARLES C THOMAS • PUBLISHER
Springfield • Illinois • U.S.A.

Published and Distributed Throughout the World by
CHARLES C THOMAS • PUBLISHER
BANNERSTONE HOUSE
301-327 East Lawrence Avenue, Springfield, Illinois, U.S.A.
NATCHEZ PLANTATION HOUSE
735 North Atlantic Boulevard, Fort Lauderdale, Florida, U.S.A.

With THOMAS BOOKS *careful attention is given to all details of
manufacturing and design. It is the Publisher's desire to present books
that are satisfactory as to their physical qualities and artistic possibilities
and appropriate for their particular use.* THOMAS BOOKS *will be true
to those laws of quality that assure a good name and good will.*

Printed in the United States of America
W-2

ACKNOWLEDGMENTS

T HIS MANUAL DERIVES from clinical experience in the Child Development Clinic of Children's Memorial Hospital. We are grateful to our patients and their parents, who are our best teachers, to our colleagues who have contributed in numerous ways, and to the hospital which encourages our work and gives us the freedom to do it.

We are deeply indebted to Miss Jean Stiman who, with unfailing good humor and unerring accuracy, has typed and retyped.

CONTENTS

TOYS AND GAMES
for
EDUCATIONALLY
HANDICAPPED CHILDREN

Toy Project

INTRODUCTION

Recent years have witnessed an explosion of interest in children with a variety of educational handicaps, ranging from general retardation to subtle disabilities in limited areas of functioning. One of the satisfying results of this interest is the development of a group of teachers trained in special education who are gradually developing a variety of useful materials for these children, both evaluative and remedial.

A gap remains, however, between the efforts of the educators and the parents of children with educational handicaps, who are usually eager to be of personal help to their child but are uncertain as to how they might best proceed. This becomes the source of much frustration to the parent and often engenders feelings of inadequacy. Some of the parents attempt to resolve the dilemma by obtaining regular curricula material and institute what amounts to a type of school program at home. This is likely to produce undesirable results for a number of reasons: availability of the materials at home removes the appeal and novelty that the material should have in school; competition between parent and teacher is encouraged; there is a possibility of producing an adverse emotional reaction to the learning experience.

In our work we frequently find ourselves dealing with this problem by recommending the use of specific toys which appear to be suitable material for a child with a particular handicap. Our interest has gradually expanded to reviewing many toy catalogs for suitable material. This manual is an effort to share the result of these efforts with others.

In preparing this material we have omitted toys that did not appear relevant, as well as some that are essentially duplicated by other manufacturers. This does not necessarily imply a preference. It is quite suitable to substitute other similar toys. Certainly there are also fine toys that are not included because

5

we overlooked them or were unaware of them. Toys change constantly and are not documented in clear-cut fashion.

Each toy is reviewed under the appropriate intellectual categories and the toys are arranged in ascending order of difficulty for that category. When a particular toy may be employed at a variety of ages, employing different levels of skills, the tendency was to place it toward the lower end of the useful spectrum. The list also includes the manufacturer, an opinion as to which sex might be interested, the general age level of interest among normal children, and a brief description. When the interest level is written as 8+ this means children eight years old and above. The latter is sometimes derived from the suggestion of the manufacturer and is to be loosely interpreted. Thus it is possible, in many instances, to find a toy that would appeal to a child of a certain mental age in combination with a particular level of ability. This is possible, since some toys are interesting and challenging yet relatively easy with respect to a particular function. A number of board games, for example, require rather simple like-difference skills yet remain interesting to children who have passed that point of maturity. This enables the child to have successes without feeling that the material is boring or insulting to his level of maturity.

The order of difficulty is based primarily on opinion and should be very loosely interpreted. In many instances different approaches seemed equally efficacious. When a high-level item is chosen for a particular child because it is not demanding in a particular area, it is important to judge whether all of the other requisite skills are at a suitable level to enable the child to play the game appropriately.

The classification scheme posed problems since, in effect, it is a way of stating how intellectual functions occur—an overly pretentious undertaking. For this reason intellectual skills have been subdivided with a relatively common type of scheme, hoping that this would be communicative, but without the belief that this furthered understanding of mental functioning.

All functions are divided into four major categories; perception, retention and recall, conceptualization, and expression.

A SCHEME FOR SUBDIVIDING THE INTELLECTUAL FUNCTIONS

		RETENTION AND		CONCEPTUAL-		
PERCEPTION		RECALL		IZATION	EXPRESSION	
Visual	*Auditory*	*Visual*	*Auditory*		*Verbal*	*Motor*
Like-difference	Like-difference	*Memory*	*Memory*			Fine
Part-whole						Gross
Spatial relations	Figure-ground					
Figure-ground						

Perception is further subdivided into visual and auditory, and each of these is further subdivided:

1. Like-difference
    This involves the perceptual aspects of such activities as matching, sorting, and categorizing objects according to physical characteristics and functions.
2. Part-whole relationships
    The ability to perceive the parts of an object in relation to the whole (included only for visual perception).
3. Spatial relations
    The ability to perceive the position of two or more objects in relation to one's self and to each other.
4. Figure-ground
    The ability to select the relevant object from the background.

Retention and recall is subdivided into auditory and visual memory.

Conceptualization is not subdivided. Subclassification did not appear possible at this time in relation to the games. The central functions are seen as complex, overlapping, and difficult to define.

Expression is subdivided into verbal and motor. There is no separate scheme for visual-motor functioning. The reason is that almost all motor functions for the included toys and games require eye-hand or eye-foot coordination; therefore, a visual-motor category would be a duplication of the motor-expression category. Motor functions are further subdivided into *fine,* principally involving oppositional use of the fingers for dexterous motions but also involving use of the arms, forearms, and hands in a relatively limited range of motion; and *gross,* involving all larger muscle activities.

The scheme is not meant to be complete, but rather to include those functions that can best be represented by toys and games.

There are two indices. The Manufacturer Index lists the name and address of each manufacturer, as well as the abbreviation used throughout the manual. The Toy Index lists each toy, the manufacturer's abbreviation, and the categories under which it appears.

The most important single thing to stress with parents is that games are meant to be fun. If these are used in a manner which the child finds objectionable, disruptive or damaging to self-concept, the results are likely to be poor. In most instances, if the toys are properly employed, the child will eagerly look forward to playing with the parent or by himself. Games obtained in this program should be reserved for use with this child, rather than shared with older or more able children if it is likely that they will provide unfair competition and discouragement. Success will make a greater contribution than will failure.

When selecting toys, it is best to choose those with an interest level that matches the child's mental age. In addition they should require skill below that of the child's ability in the area in which the child is handicapped. Initially this might mean employing toys that have only slight requirements in the area of handicap. Gradually, more difficult toys are introduced, commensurate with an increase in the child's ability. Great patience is required, since progress may be quite slow. At the same time one must be attentive and responsive to the child's personal preferences.

Playing can be very hard on the parent as well as on the child. The child will sense when the parent becomes irritated or bored. It is best to stop before this point is reached. Having very brief play sessions which are mutually satisfactory is much better than having longer ones which end with hurt feelings.

VISUAL PERCEPTION

LIKE-DIFFERENT

E ACH PERSON'S ENVIRONMENT presents a continuous kaleido-
scope containing myriad details which, if dealt with individually,
would lead to chaos. There are a number of ways that this is
handled in the normal course of events. One, dealt with else-
where, is by distinguishing the object which must be attended
to from those which are irrelevant. This is referred to as the
figure-ground function. The present section relates to the han-
dling of details by sorting, grouping, matching, and categorizing.
This ability enables the examination of a new stimulus from a
variety of reference points which have been previously established
and then allows one to react in a manner which is predicated
upon prior experiences. This function is a vital one and per
meates almost all cognitive functions.

Actually, there are probably a variety of intellectually
separable tasks subsumed in this category, placed together only
by the lack of more sophistication in the field.

In items such as bead-stringing, parquetry blocks, and design
tiles, the child can be requested to copy designs made by the
parents. With construction toys the child can copy both the
parent's objects and the items demonstrated on the instruction
sheets included with the materials.

		INTEREST	
NAME OF TOY	MANUFACTURER	Sex	Age
Sandbox Play	**Many**	**Both**	**2-5**
Give the child different-sized bottles, cans, jars, funnels, pans, sieves for filling and dumping the sand.			
Giant Rack-A-Stack	**FPT**	**Both**	**1-3**
Ten rings fit on a cane in size sequence.			

NAME OF TOY	MANUFACTURER	INTEREST	
		Sex	*Age*

Form Boxes   PMC   Both   1½-5
  1. Postal Station
  2. Lock-up Barn
Child fits twelve varicolored blocks of four shapes into respective slots in the tops of the boxes.

Goldilocks and The Three
  Bears Playhouse   FPT   Both   2-5
The geometrically shaped figures must be matched to the slots in the top of the playhouse.

Indian Beads   PMC   Both   2-4
Large beads for stringing.

Beads for Stringing   MBC   Both   2-6
Different shapes, sizes, and colors.

Coordination Board   SIF   Both   2-4
Four geometric shapes in different colors in a puzzle form. The child must match a cutout to the appropriate space.

Shapes, Colors and Forms   CCE   Both   2-4
Rubber forms of graduated sizes fit into a wooden tray.

Peg and Shape Sort Board   BSC   Both   2-5
Four geometric wooden shapes with holes in them to fit on pegs attached to a board.

Creative Blocks   FPT   Both   1-4
Plastic blocks fit over wooden dowels.

Nuts and Bolts   HCM   Both   1½-3
Sturdy plastic threaded bolt serves as base on which to fit four large nuts.

NAME OF TOY	MANUFACTURER	INTEREST	
		Sex	*Age*

Nuts and Bolts   **CCE**   Both   2-4

Nuts and bolts made of plastic must be matched by color and size.

Tinker Box   **CHI**   Both   2-4

Plastic tool box into which large screws, nuts, and bolts can be put with the aid of a plastic hammer, a screwdriver, and a wrench.

Lots-A-Links   **AMS**   Both   3-5

Plastic multicolored snap-close links which can make chains, bracelets, et cetera.

Spin 'N' Color   **MBC**   Both   4-9

A competitive game to match colors. The first one to finish wins. Twenty-seven pictures with wipe-off surface and crayons.

Hickety Pickety   **PAR**   Both   3-5

Child must place a colored egg in a nest of a color that matches that color pointed to by spinner.

Winnie-The-Pooh   **PAR**   Both   4-8

Child reaches into a grab bag for a colored disc which tells him where to move his player.

Three Little Pigs   **SRC**   Both   4-8

This game is based on the story of the Three Little Pigs. Players move by matching colors.

Fortune   **PAR**   Both   4-10

A marble game played by spinning a color wheel. The object is to capture all marbles of one color.

NAME OF TOY	MANUFACTURER	INTEREST	
		Sex	Age

Topper   **LAK**   **Both**   **4-8**

A spinner indicates colors which can be matched on the board. The player who fills his spaces first wins.

Toot! Toot!   **SRC**   **Both**   **4-8**

This game requires no reading or counting—simply matching moves with colors drawn.

Children's Hour   **PAR**   **Both**   **4-8**

Three games in one: Peanut the Elephant, Porky the Pig, and ABC Fishing. This requires only color-matching.

Candy Land   **MBC**   **Both**   **4-8**

No reading involved. Draw a card and move to the corresponding color or object.

Twister   **MBC**   **Both**   **8+**

Two players put all four extremities on colored circles on a plastic game rug. A spinner shows where the player must move his hands and feet next. This requires a sense of balance. This is a game played by older children and adults but requires low-level color-matching.

Jumbo Color Dominoes   **PMC**   **Both**   **3-6**
                                    MBC   **Both**   **5-10**

Color dot dominoes for visual matching to teach counting and colors.

Color Bingo   **EUC**   **Both**   **5-8**

Teaches color and number identification.

Crayon Coloring Cards   **SGH**   **Both**   **5-8**

Ten stencil cards showing colors to be used to teach the first steps in drawing. Crayons are supplied.

NAME OF TOY	MANUFACTURER	INTEREST	
		Sex	*Age*

Sand Art Drawing Set RBI Both 10+

Contains twelve picture cards, colored sand, sand pen, and glue. Requires color-matching.

Voice Books MCI Both 1½-4

Each picture on the cover hides the appropriate voice, and eight illustrated pages show the object in various situations. The voice sounds when the child touches the cover. This toy is a combination visual-auditory like-different.

Barnyard Voices MCI Both 2-5

Wooden cylinders which can be tipped to produce an animal sound. Pictures are painted on the outside.

Beginner Inlay Puzzles SIF Both 1½-5

Each picture is one separate unit that fits only one space. There are five to six pictures per wooden frame. **Note:** Puzzles were believed to represent a more complex matching skill than simple color-matching.

Playboards SIM Both 2-5

Simple, one-piece wooden puzzles with knobs. Pictures of familiar objects.

Round Puzzles MCI Both 1½-4

Wooden one-piece and multipiece puzzles with and without knobs.

Animal and Bird Fun AMS Both 5-7

Cards with colored animal pictures on them. Animal heads are cut out as well as names and must be matched to cards.

Rainbow Towers SGH Both 4-7

Game involving skills prerequisite for learning to count using colored-bead towers.

| NAME OF TOY | MANUFACTURER | INTEREST | |
		Sex	Age

Difference Puzzles   SIM   Both   3-6
Puzzles teach difference of shapes and sizes of objects.

Peg Leveling Board   BSC   Both   2-5
Nine wooden pegs, graduated in size, fit into holes in a board.

Noah's Ark   Many   Both   4-6
The spinner directs players to place an animal in the large cardboard ark.

Fun Cards   PAR   Both   3-5
Child must fit die-cut animals and letters spelling their names into large individual board.

Stacking Toys   MCI   Both   2-4
An elephant, an owl, and a Mexican man made of several wooden pieces which are stacked in a precise order.

Peg Grading Board   BSC   Both   2-5
Child must sort and grade thirty wooden pegs for size and color to fit into a board with thirty holes.

Fit-A-Square   CCE   Both   2-4
Teaches child colors and form association by providing him with sixteen cutout rubber discs into which forty-eight pieces in twelve different shapes fit.

Judgments and Readiness   CPT   Both   4-8
Colored rubber squares, circles, and triangles are composed of five or more concentric outlines which can be taken apart and fit together to make a solid figure.

Counting Frame   PMC   Both   3-8
Wooden beads slide on rods on a large frame. Helps child learn basic colors and simple arithmetic.

NAME OF TOY	MANUFACTURER	INTEREST	
		Sex	Age

One-To-Ten Counting Books   MCI   Both   3-5

Colorful books which encourage the child to associate number symbols with appropriate number of objects.

Picture Word-Builder   MBC   Both   3-8

Thirty-six cards with pictures and names. Cutout section with duplicate word to be matched.

Matchettes   CPT   Both   4-6

Matching cards are paired to pictures on a board. Ten boards per set.

Playskool Match-ups   PMC   Both   3-6
1. **Picture Alphabet**
2. **Colors and Things**
3. **Count From 1-24**
4. **Words to Spell**
5. **Animal Homes**
6. **People and Their Jobs**
Two-piece match-up cards.

Liddle Kiddle Games   MTI   Both   4-7
1. **Baby Animals**
2. **Let's Go Fishing**
3. **Color Bingo**
In each game the child must match the top and bottom halves of pictures.

Match Mates   CPT   Both   3-6

Ten jigsaw puzzles, cut in half, have numbers on the top half to correspond with the number of objects on the bottom. Tops and bottoms fit only when correctly matched.

Cinderella   PAR   Girls   5-10

A board game based on the fairy tale. Cards control players moves.

NAME OF TOY	MANUFACTURER	INTEREST	
		Sex	*Age*

Landscape Peg Set PMC Both 2½-6

Child constructs landscapes with pegs and wooden shapes.
Note: Most construction toys offer a wide range of possibilities
for like-different skills.

Design Tiles SIF Both 3-6

Large plastic honeycomb-shaped tiles can be fitted into brilliant
designs. Six colored keysheets are included.

Parquetry Blocks PMC Both 3-6

Various-shaped wooden blocks fit together to make colorful
designs. Design suggestions included. **Note:** Child can be
required to copy designs made by the parent.

Colorforms CCE Both 4-7

Make designs with die-cut plastic shapes which adhere to a
plastic workboard.

Design Blocks CCE Both 4-7

Square colored wooden blocks. Child combines solid colors
and diagonals to form endless designs.

Hex SGH Both 4-8

Eighty hexagon printed cards are matched according to color
and design to form flowers.

Jolly Time Dominoes MBC Both 4-7

Colored pictures on one side and regular dominoes on the
reverse side. The object is to match.

Animal Dominoes FAR Both 4-7

The object is to match the animals to those that have been
played.

		INTEREST	
NAME OF TOY	MANUFACTURER	*Sex*	*Age*

Picture Dominoes   HAR   Both   4-7

Twenty-eight dominoes with pictures on one side and dots on the other.

Sorting Box Combination   MCI   Both   4-8

This toy is designed to teach colors and numbers. Wooden strips of different colors and with objects painted on them are matched to master strips.

Counting Dominoes   CPT   Both   5-8

Players are given equal number of cards and must match pictures to pictures, pictures to numbers, or numbers to numbers until all cards are gone.

Puzzle—Lotto Games   EUC   Both   4-7

1. **On the Farm**
2. **Around the House**

Playing cards showing parts of a picture must be matched to the same picture on the playing board.

Lotto   EUC   Both   4-8

1. **ABC Lotto**   5. **What's Missing Lotto**
2. **Zoo Lotto**   6. **Go-Together Lotto**
3. **Farm Lotto**   7. **Object Lotto**
4. **The World About Us Lotto**

The child must match the picture cards to pictures on the playing boards.

Fit-In-Picture Lotto   SGH   Both   4-8

Forty-eight picture shapes must be matched to outline on a master card.

Spell By Pictures   WAC   Both   4-6

Three movable bands of pictures are manipulated until three identical pictures are lined up and the correct spelling is found at the bottom.

NAME OF TOY	MANUFACTURER	INTEREST Sex	Age

Spell Master   SGH   Both   4-7

One hundred pictures with names to spell and eighty plastic letters, so constructed that only the correct letters fit.

Slate Bingo   WAC   Both   4-8

A bingo game where children learn their ABC's. Spinner dial shows twenty-four objects that are matched on cards along with letters.

Old Maid   MBC   Both   5-8

This card game requires no reading or number concept, since it is played by matching pictures.

Pardon Me   PAR   Both   5-8

A card game. Play calls for simple counting and matching of pictures of animals.

Thistle   PAR   Both   6-12

A card game. Players match cards by drawing or picking up opponent's card.

Addams Family Card Game   MBC   Both   7-15

Battles take place among the Addams Family when cards match.

Voyage to the Botton of the Sea   MBC   Both   7-15

Two card games in one. Players must follow suit or pick up discards.

Raggedy Ann   MBC   Both   4-9

Players complete Raggedy Ann's picture using cards obtained by matching pictures on a spinner with those on the playing board.

NAME OF TOY	MANUFACTURER	INTEREST	
		Sex	*Age*

Go-Together Cards   EUC   Both   4-6
Match bottoms to tops of animal cards.

Goat   MBC   Both   3-8
Playing cards are sections of animal pictures. They must be traded and paired to complete the picture.

Gingerbread Man   SRC   Both   6-10
Players progress along a path filled with matching pieces of various parts of a gingerbread house. Pieces are accumulated to build the house.

Floundering   SGH   Both   6-10
Players take turns throwing dice and putting together a fish. The parts show a number which must match the dice thrown.

Car Capers   SGH   Both   5+
Players take turns throwing dice and assembling cars in puzzle form.

Giant Snap-Lock Ring and Beads FPT   Both   2-4
Colored plastic parts snap together to make chains, et cetera.

Snap 'N' Play   SIF   Both   4-7
Wooden pieces of various shapes and sizes snap together to make objects.

Matching and Sorting Cards   EUC   Both   4-7
1. Play Store
2. Play House
Six different stores or rooms of a house with thirty-six items to be put into store or house.

NAME OF TOY	MANUFACTURER	INTEREST	
		Sex	*Age*

Operation — MBC — Both — 6+

Pick-up cards determine the type of operation the player must make on a plastic man with removable plastic parts. The part must be removed carefully with a tweezer in order to score points.

Chaos — AMS — Both — 5-10

Game contains ninety-six playing pieces and eight playing cards. The object is to fill your card with matching die-cut parts.

Contact — PAR — Both — 6+

Players must match numbers and colors of thirty-six triangle counters.

Dominoes — HAL — Both — 6+
MBC — Both — 6+

The regular domino game which requires matching and number skills.

Crow — PAR — Both — 4-12

A card game to play when traveling. Players match objects they see with cards.

Car Travel Game — MBC — Both — 5-12

Four games in one. Players match colors and objects they pass while traveling.

Picture Plaques — CPT — Both — 4-6

The plaques are superficially similar, but children must make fine discriminations to match.

Krupferli — CPT — Both — 4-8

Plastic components for making chains, shapes, baskets, and geometric forms.

NAME OF TOY	MANUFACTURER	INTEREST	
		Sex	*Age*

Funblocks SIF Both 4-12

Plastic interlocking blocks shaped like snowflakes. The set includes closed links, open links, corners, et cetera for endless combinations.

Hammer and Nail Set HAL Both 4-7

Pounding board 12" by 10". Colored heads of Huck, Yogi, and others in chipboard. Laying sticks, nails, and hammer are used to create humorous scenes.

Hammer and Nail Set CCE Both 4-6

Set includes a board, hammer, object blocks, nails, and sticks to be used in creating pictures on a wallboard.

Picture Beads HAL Both 4-10

Small beads push into white Styrofoam to create pictures from a design sheet.

Plaquette-Mosaic Wall Hanging GCC Girls 8-14

Make picture wall hangings using precut mosaic shapes and glue.

Play Chest HCM Both 3-5

Wooden chest complete with blackboard, pegboard, mallet, and pegs.

Peg Desk PMC Both 3-8

Desk with attached seat. Top of desk is a blackboard. Chalk and eraser are supplied. Under the top is a pegboard. Pegs are supplied.

Rubber Beaded Pegboards CPT Both 4-8

Duplicate or make designs with pegs on the board.

NAME OF TOY	MANUFACTURER	INTEREST	
		Sex	*Age*

Tinker Toys   Many   Both   3-8

Assorted wooden Tinker Toy pieces and moving parts used for construction.

Parquetry Blocks   MBC   Both   5-10

Various-shaped wooden blocks fit together to make colorful designs. Design suggestions included.

Pegboard Playtiles   HAL   Both   5-10

This set includes 448 plastic tiles in three different shapes which fit snugly into pegboard to create mosaic designs and pictures.

HammerNail Design Board Set   CPT   Both   5-10

Two hundred varied die-cut steel shapes. Hammer and nails are used to construct designs on wallboards.

Magnasticks   CCE   Both   5-7

Magnetic plates hold metal construction parts together while building structures.

Rig-A-Jig   CCE   Both   5-7

Colorful plastic pieces interlock to form people, animals, trucks, and geometric forms.

Go Fish   Many   Both   5-8

Played with a regular or special deck of cards. Players match and collect books of similar cards.

Zorro   PAR   Both   5-10

Players move their men down the path to make a rescue. Moves are controlled by dice. This game involves number concepts and matching.

NAME OF TOY	MANUFACTURER	INTEREST Sex	Age
Mary Poppins	PAR	Both	5-10

A board game based on the movie, with the same story and characters. Moves are controlled by a throw of the dice.

Bingo	SRC	Both	6+
	MBC	Both	6+
	FAR	Both	6+

The original Bingo game where the caller calls the numbers and players cover the numbers in an attempt to get a Bingo.

Pairs—Word Game	MBC	Both	6-9

Contains three sets of cards to match: picture-picture, picture-word, word-word.

Picture Lotto Assortment	MBC	Both	5-12

1. **Look and Learn**—pictures, letters, and words
2. **Geography**—shapes, sizes, capitals, products
3. **Animal**—animals, picture-word and word-word
4. **Word-Building**—object-word, pronounce and spell

Key-Kit Spelling	SHI	Both	4-7

Colorful picture cards with alphabet letters to spell the name of the object. Key-cards are notched, so that only the correct letters fit. A coloring workbook is included.

Key-Kit Spelling	SHI	Both	5-8

Colorful picture cards with alphabet letters to spell the name of the object. Key-cards are notched, so that only the correct letters fit. A coloring workbook is included.

Key-Kit Arithmetic	SHI	Both	4-7

Colorful picture cards are notched, so that only the correct number fits, to teach basic number concepts. A coloring workbook is included.

NAME OF TOY	MANUFACTURER	INTEREST	
		Sex	*Age*

Table Mat Stenciling   SGH   **Girls**   8-14

Seven coasters on which water-resistant pictures are painted with the aid of stencils.

Construction Kit   MCI   **Both**   3-5

Nuts, bolts, and connectors (wooden) are joined to form objects and toys.

Wood Toy Builder   PMC   **Both**   3-8

Construction kit consists of wooden girders, nuts, bolts, screws, and appropriate plastic tools.

Flexagons   CCE   **Both**   5-8

Four cardboard squares and triangles assemble with rubber bands to form 3-D boats, houses, and geometric forms.

Wooden Plane   MCI   **Both**   3-8

Forty-three wooden pieces including nuts, bolts, and connectors which can be used for construction of many objects.

Bolt-It   CPT   **Both**   4-8

Large wooden, plastic, and metal parts to make rolling and stationary toys from suggested designs.

Hardwood Construction Set   MCI   **Both**   3-7

Fifty building parts—nuts, bolts, screws, drilled strips, pulleys, and four rubber tires. Wooden wrench, screwdriver, and guide booklet provided.

Bolts and Nuts Builder   KOH   **Both**   4-6

Large wooden and plastic bolts, nuts, wheels, and other parts can be combined to form movable toys.

		INTEREST	
NAME OF TOY	MANUFACTURER	*Sex*	*Age*

Asymmetric Space Construction   CPT   Both   4-8

Sixty pieces of various-sized rods and dowels for construction of various objects.

Lincoln Logs   PMC   Both   4-8

     HAL   Both   4-8

Three-quarter-inch hardwood logs and other material for construction of buildings.

Flower Craft   BSC   Girls   5-8

Make your own floral arrangements. Flower parts are provided with complete instructions.

Flower Basket   SGH   Girls   6-10

A tray full of plastic flower parts to make floral decoration. Plastic baskets and weaving material are provided.

Sewing Machine Set   HCM   Girls   5-8

Sets include miniature machine that operates by hand. Needles, thread, thimble, scissors, patterns, and material are also included.

Luggage Sewing Assortment   HCM   Girls   5-8

Three different sets—embroidery, sewing, and stitch-a-story. All necessary materials included.

Loom Craft   HCM   Girls   5-12

Various-size looms and cotton loopers to weave to make pot holders, et cetera. Designs can be copied or created.

Braiding   Many   Both   5-12

Braid simple lanyards out of colored plastic laces.

NAME OF TOY	MANUFACTURER	INTEREST	
		Sex	*Age*

Basket Making   SGH   Girls   5-8

Includes precut sticks and paper strips with instructions for making six baskets.

Raffia Baskets   SGH   Girls   6-9

Includes four colored plastic basket shapes and raffia for weaving.

Weave-A-Basket   SGH   Girls   6-9

Includes four colored basket shapes and raffia for weaving.

Woolly Pictures   SGH   Girls   8-12

Six framed pictures are to be stitched to make miniature tapestries. Needles, wool, and guide sheet are supplied.

Jewelry Craft Assortment   HCM   Girls   7-10

Four different sets—charms and chains, snap-in beads, Indian beads, and stone bracelets—all for creating your own jewelry.

Block City   CCE   Both   4-8

These sets supply plastic interlocking blocks cut for building houses, stores, and buildings.

Lego System Blocks   CCE   Both   4-8

Interlocking blocks of different shapes and primary colors can be combined to form sturdy structures.

American Plastic Bricks   HAL   Both   5-8

Interlocking plastic bricks can be used to create many different objects.

Inventatoy   CPT   Both   4-8

Dowels and connector parts can be manipulated to form toys with movable parts.

Snap-Eze Playforms   **CCE**   **Both**   **5-7**
A collection of unbreakable plastic rods, wheels, and blocks all interlocking to build a wide range of objects (e.g. people, houses, cars).

Creating With Wood   **Many**   **Boys**   **5+**
Use tools and a pattern to make simple objects (e.g. go-carts, simple furniture).

Super Puzzle   **SGH**   **Both**   **7+**
Sixty silhouette puzzles to be solved using plastic shapes. Instruction book and solutions included.

Constructo Straws   **PAR**   **Both**   **6-10**
Two hundred flexible plastic straws can be joined to make large-scale models.

Bend 'N' Build Construction Set **CCE**   **Both**   **6-10**
Big unbreakable plastic tubes for construction of large-scale models. Connectors link tubes and parts are movable.

Geodestix Construction Kit   **CPT**   **Both**   **6-12**
Sturdy rods and plastic connector joints can be manipulated to form interesting 3-D designs.

Building Models   **Many**   **Boys**   **6-14**
Precut plastic or wooden parts must be glued together following a pattern to make objects such as cars, boats, planes.

Smarty   **EFG**   **Both**   **7-12**
Arithmetic-Bingo game which teaches addition and subtraction.

Ship in Bottle   **CPT**   **Boys**   **8-12**
Child must glue precut parts of a boat and then place in bottle which is then glued together.

NAME OF TOY	MANUFACTURER	INTEREST	
		Sex	*Age*

Junior Electro-Experimental Set   RBI   Boys   10-16

Child learns the principle of electricity by putting together simple, safe, everyday components.

Erector Set   GIL   Boys   8+

A variety of metal building components and an electric motor for building structures.

Indian Bead Craft   WAL   Both   8-14

Decorate belts, moccasins, and other precut leather objects with Indian beads. Involves stringing beads into a design.

Embroidery Set   PAR   Girls   5-8

Child decorates a prestamped doll bedspread and pillow set. All necessary material included.

Mat Embroidery   SGH   Girls   8-12

Four colored linen mats printed with easy-to-follow designs. Yarn and frame are supplied.

Mary Poppins Needlepoint Set   HCM   Girls   6-10

Tapestry, yarn, and needle are supplied. Finished product can be framed.

Weaving Loom   SGH   Both   10+

Children can make scarves, mats, et cetera on miniature looms. Comes with instructions for designing articles.

Knitting   Many   Girls   10+

Knitting with various regulation-size needles using different weight yarns and following a pattern.

Sewing   Many   Girls   10+

Sewing by hand or with the aid of a machine, using regular patterns and various types of materials.

NAME OF TOY	MANUFACTURER	INTEREST *Sex*	*Age*

Junior Memory Game   CPT   Both   4-10

Child must remember location of matching cards. Cards may also be used as cues for story-telling.

Children's Hour   CCE   Both   5-10

Three games in one which combines picture and alphabet identification with beginning number and reading skills.

Poster Stencil Set   FAR   Both   6-10

Cardboard stencils—1 to 1½" high capital and lowercase letters, numerals, et cetera.

Match-Ums   HAR   Both   5-8

Match twenty-eight pictures to twenty-eight words.

Alphabet Sorting Tray Kit   MBC   Both   5-8

Individual compartments on a board for sorting letters and building simple words.

Alphabet Picture Flash Cards   MBC   Both   5-7

Colored pictures of objects and alphabet letters. Games teach letter recognition and spelling.

Dial Speller   HAR   Both   6-10

Learn to spell by association with picture and alphabet dials. Chalk, eraser, and blackboard included. Spell the word and write the word.

Phonetic Quizmo   MBC   Both   6-8

Parent says sound; child finds letter or letters on card. Similar to Lotto.

Sentence Builder   MBC   Both   6-10

Alphabet letters and basic words, to build words and sentences.

NAME OF TOY	MANUFACTURER	INTEREST	
		Sex	*Age*

Beginning Consonant Poster Cards   MBC   Both   6-10

Cards have a picture and a word with one or two missing letters. The child must identify the missing letters and pronounce the word.

Vowel-Links Poster Cards   MBC   Both   6-10

Cards have pictures and words with one or two missing letters. The child must insert the missing letters and pronounce the word.

Educational Concentration   MBC   Both   7-12

Four categories: color-matching, word-matching, states, and history.

Phonetic Word Builder   MBC   Both   7-12

Build words, using individual cards with consonants, consonant blends, special blends, double vowels, and short and long vowel endings.

Arithmetic Quizmo   MBC   Both   7-12

Played similar to Lotto. Practice in addition, subtraction, multiplication, and division.

Memory Game   MBC   Both   10+

Players use their memory to locate and collect matching pairs of picture cards.

Concentration   MBC   Both   10+

Players move numbered slides to find matching gift cards. As matches are made, more of the puzzle is revealed on the board. The first to solve the puzzle wins.

NAME OF TOY	MANUFACTURER	INTEREST	
		Sex	*Age*

Authors PAR Both 8+

A card game. The object is to collect complete sets of authors and their works.

Paper Plays CPT Both 8-12

Patterned paper is folded and cut to form 3-D sculptures.

String Figures CPT Both 10+

An instruction booklet tells how to create 105 designs out of string.

Knot Tying Board CPT Boys 10+

Booklet, practice board, and rope, to learn various methods of tying knots.

Junior Clockmaker Kit RBI Boys 10+

Put a real cuckoo clock together and make it run.

Facts-In-Five AIC Both 9+

Players are assigned five letters and five categories of subject matter. See how many words or names you can come up with that start with the assigned letter and fit the classification.

PART-WHOLE

The ability to understand the relationship between individual parts of an object and the whole is a basic one in intellectual functioning. The development, for example, of a suitable body image requires a detailed knowledge of the interrelationships among the body parts. As adults, the part-whole problems that are encountered are usually simple because they are familiar, although assembly of a novel gadget (or even a children's toy) may cause frustrating and embarrassing moments. It is easy to comprehend the difficulty young children have in perceiving part-whole relationships by observing their drawings, particularly those of the human figure.

The grading of the skill required to perform games in this category was based on the number and size of the parts as well as the number of dimensions of the object. Construction of words requires perception of part-whole relationships in terms of symbols rather than realistic objects and is considered to be a more difficult task.

		INTEREST	
NAME OF TOY	MANUFACTURER	*Sex*	*Age*

Blocks — PMC — Both — 1½-8

Colored and plain wooden blocks of varied shapes and sizes for building. **Note:** Blocks, as well as other construction toys, have a wide range of applicability in developing the part-whole concept.

Giant Rack-A-Stack — FPT — Both — 1-3

Ten rings fit on a cane in size sequence.

Miniature Series — MCI — Both — 1½-4

Vivid picture stories of familiar subject matter such as shopping, the farm, the zoo, in 3-D.

Hi-Lo Interlocking Blocks — HAL — Both — 1½-4

Indented alphabet letters on 1½" blocks that interlock for ease in building.

Creative Blocks — FPT — Both — 1-4

Plastic blocks fit over wooden dowels.

Nuts and Bolts — HCM — Both — 1½-3

Sturdy plastic threaded bolt serves as base on which to fit four large nuts.

NAME OF TOY	MANUFACTURER	INTEREST	
		Sex	*Age*

Nuts and Bolts CCE Both 2-4

Nuts and bolts made of plastic must be matched for size and color.

Bags of Blocks HAL Both 2-5

Colored and natural finish ⅞" scale wood blocks in ten different shapes.

Educational Blocks FPT Both 2-5

Varied shaped wooden blocks for building.

Sandbox Play Many Both 2-5

Give the child different-sized bottles, cans, jars, funnels, pans, sieves for filling and dumping the sand.

Boo Boo Blocks LAK Both 2-5

Match heads and bodies of animals painted on interlocking two-piece blocks.

Round Puzzles MCI Both 1½-4

Wooden one-piece and multipiece puzzles with and without knobs. **Note:** Jigsaw puzzles, existing at all levels of complexity, are of great value for creating a graded part-whole series.

Clay MBC Both 3+

1. **Clayrite**
2. **Tru-Model**

Artificial clay used to create objects. May be reused again and again.

NAME OF TOY	MANUFACTURER	INTEREST	
		Sex	*Age*

Clay Modeling CPT Both 3+
  1. **Playdough or artificial clay**
  2. **Modo clay**—hardens without firing
  3. **Cera clay**—oven fire at home
  4. **Pottery clay**—must be fired at high temperatures
  Objects can be painted or glazed.

Sculpey PLY Both 3+
Polyform
  Plastic modeling material does not harden in the air, but hardens when baked in home oven. Objects can be carved and painted.

Popkins HCM Both 2-4
  Six different plastic heads pop together to make many characters.

Bag of Blocks and Rods HAL Both 3-5
  Wooden ⅞" building blocks in eleven different shapes; ½" diameter wooden rods are used to attach blocks.

Go-Together Cards EUC Both 4-6
  Match bottoms to tops of animal cards.

Match Mates CPT Both 3-6
  Ten jigsaw puzzles, cut in half, have numbers on the top half to correspond with the number of objects on the bottom. Tops and bottoms fit only when correctly matched.

Animal Fun MBC Both 3-8
  Animals are fitted into appropriate jungle scenes. Letters are provided so the child can spell out the animal's names upon identification.

NAME OF TOY	MANUFACTURER	INTEREST Sex	Age

Stacking Toys   MCI   Both   2-4

An elephant, an owl, and a Mexican man made of several wooden pieces which are stacked in a precise order.

Sewing Cards   FAR   Girls   4-7

Six sewing cards and yarn which can be made into two story books.

Live Cartoons   MBC   Both   4-7

Cartoon scenes and characters to punch out and set up into stories. Child tells story.

Landscape Peg Set   PMC   Both   2½-6

Child constructs landscapes with pegs and wooden shapes.

Peg Desk   PMC   Both   3-8

Desk with attached seat. Top of desk is a blackboard. Chalk and eraser are supplied. Under the top is a pegboard. Pegs are supplied.

Play Chest   HCM   Both   3-5

Wooden chest complete with blackboard, pegboard, mallet, and pegs.

New Tot Railroad   PMC   Both   2-9

Twenty-eight-piece plastic railroad set for beginners. Child builds in many ways.

Skaneateles Transportation Sets   PMC   Both   2-10

Wooden railroad sets—tracks, cars, et cetera.

NAME OF TOY	MANUFACTURER	INTEREST	
		Sex	*Age*

Playskool Match-Ups   PMC   Both   3-6
   1. **Picture Alphabet**
   2. **Colors and Things**
   3. **Count From 1-24**
   4. **Words to Spell**
   5. **Animal Homes**
   6. **People and Their Jobs**
Two-piece match-up cards.

Liddle Kiddle Games   MTI   Both   4-7
   1. **Baby Animals**
   2. **Let's Go Fishing**
   3. **Color Bingo**
In each game, the child must match the top and bottom halves of pictures.

Juvenile Jigsaw Puzzles   SIF   Both   3-6
Two puzzles per box—each puzzle contains six pieces which are made out of durable material.

Puzzle—Lotto Games   EUC   Both   4-7
   1. **On the Farm**
   2. **Around the House**
Playing cards showing parts of a picture must be matched to the same picture on the playing board.

Puzzle Cubes   MCI   Both   4-7
Twelve cubes can be made into six different color pictures. Guides are included in box.

Simple Things To Color   PMC   Both   4-7
Large pictures to color for young children.

Sew A Toy   MBC   Both   4-10
Chipboard is sewn together to make wallet, band, jewelry box, et cetera. Materials are included for decorating them.

NAME OF TOY	MANUFACTURER	INTEREST	
		Sex	*Age*

Make Your Own Action Puppets   MBC   Both   4-10

Six puppet figures and materials used to assemble them including crayons.

Mix-Nix   AMS   Both   4-7

Child changes both body and facial characteristics of heavy cardboard figures by adding 3-D parts.

Doodle Dialer   WAC   Both   4-10

Thousands of combinations to form faces by simply turning four different dials.

Leather Craft   Many   Both   5-12

Use precut patterns or cut your own and punch holes in it and lace together to make useful items such as billfolds and moccasins. **Note:** Hobby items, particularly those which result in a useful product, have appeal for all ages yet may be relatively undemanding in selected areas.

Playmates   SGH   Girls   7-10

Four precut animal shapes to be stitched together and stuffed. All necessary articles furnished.

Leather Craft   RBI   Both   8+

Contains precut leather parts for lacing and decorating with paint. They can be made into key chain purses, billfolds, et cetera.

Burn-Rite Leather Craft   RBI   Boys   10+

Precut leather parts and necessary equipment for tooling and burning decorations. Many useful objects to make.

Balance Building Set   MCI   Both   5-10

Fifteen odd-shaped blocks for building towers.

NAME OF TOY	MANUFACTURER	INTEREST	
		Sex	*Age*

Notchies CPT Both 3-5

Large plastic blocks interlock in various positions to assist the child in building precarious forms.

Interslot MCI Both 4-8

Thirty-four wooden pieces in six different shapes can be fit together to create structures.

Magnetic Construction Set BSC Both 2-6

Horseshoe magnet, a number of disc and bar magnets, and various-shaped metal pieces for constructing objects.

Mr. Builder's Home Workshop HAR Both 3-5

Ten plastic tools, nails, and lumber for construction.

Standard Hammer-Nail Set PMC Both 3-6

Twelve-inch square composition pounding board, laying sticks, nails, and hammer. Design sheet provided.

Construction Kit MCI Both 3-5

Nuts, bolts, and connectors (wooden) are joined to form objects and toys.

Wood Toy Builder PMC Both 3-8

Construction kit consists of wooden girders, nuts, bolts, screws and appropriate plastic tools.

Changeable Blocks HAL Both 4-7

Over four million faces can be created by piecing the blocks in different manners.

Wood Playmates CPT Both 4-6

Seven wood bodies, four heads, and a quantity of arms and legs go together to make people.

NAME OF TOY	MANUFACTURER	INTEREST	
		Sex	*Age*

Giant Snap-Lock Ring and Beads   FPT   Both   2-4
Colored plastic parts snap together to make chains, et cetera.

Snap 'N' Play   SIF   Both   4-7
Wooden pieces of various shapes and sizes snap together to make objects.

Parquetry Blocks   PMC   Both   3-6
Various-shaped wooden blocks fit together to make colorful designs. Design suggestions are included.

Design Tiles   SIF   Both   3-6
Large plastic honeycomb-shaped tiles can be fitted into brilliant designs. Six colored keysheets are included.

Design Blocks   CCE   Both   4-7
Square colored wooden blocks. Child combines solid colors and diagonals to form endless designs.

Animal and Bird Fun   AMS   Both   5-7
Cards with colored animal pictures on them. Animal heads as well as names are cut out and must be matched to cards.

Toddler Inlay Puzzles   SIF   Both   2-6
Wooden puzzles of familiar objects ranging from 5-20 pieces.

Puzzles   PMC   Both   2-6
  1. **Primary Puzzles**—1-12 pieces
  2. **Intermediate Puzzles**—10-19 pieces
  3. **Advanced Puzzles**—15-27 pieces

Boy and Girl Jigsaw Puzzle   BSC   Both   3-5
Fourteen pieces of children's clothing can be combined in different ways to complete the wooden puzzles.

NAME OF TOY	MANUFACTURER	INTEREST	
		Sex	*Age*

**Fairy Tale and Mother
  Goose Puzzles** SIF Both 3-7
  Wooden puzzles ranging from ten to twenty-five pieces.

Alphabet Inlay Puzzles SIF Both 3-7
  Wooden puzzles ranging from fifteen to thirty pieces.

Wooden Puzzles VIC Both 4-7
  Simple wooden puzzles of familiar scenes and several alphabet puzzles.

Nail-On Tiles SGH Both 4-6
  Plastic tiles, nails, wooden hammer, and board are provided for creating pictures and designs. Illustration sheet included.

Parquetry Blocks MBC Both 5-10
  Various-shaped wooden blocks fit together to make colorful designs. Design suggestions included.

Puzzles WAC Both 4-8
  1. **Mother Goose**—12 piece cardboard
  2. **Little Helper**—18 piece cardboard
  3. **Story Time**—30 piece cardboard

Comic Corner CCE Both 3-5
  Thirty-four interchangeable pegged parts to make your own street scenes. People, traffic light, and store parts are included.

Loony Links AMS Both 5-8
  Snap parts of bodies together to form animals and people.

Spin 'N' Color MBC Both 4-9
  A competitive game to see colors. The first to finish wins. Twenty-seven pictures with wipe-off surface and crayons.

NAME OF TOY	MANUFACTURER	INTEREST Sex	Age

Glitter Color Kit MBC Both 5-12

Contains stencils and two types of paint—Glitter Tone and Silk Tone.

Crayon Coloring Cards SGH Both 5-8

Ten stencil cards showing colors to be used to teach the first steps in drawing. Crayons are supplied.

Goat MBC Both 3-8

Playing cards are sections of animal pictures. They must be traded and paired to complete the picture.

Raggedy Ann MBC Both 4-9

Players complete Raggedy Ann's picture using cards obtained by matching pictures on a spinner with those on the playing board.

Chaos AMS Both 5-10

Game contains ninety-six playing pieces and eight playing cards. The object is to fill your card with matching die-cut parts first.

Floundering SGH Both 6-10

Players take turns throwing dice and putting together a fish. The parts show a number which must match the dice thrown.

Car Capers SGH Both 5+

Players take turns throwing dice and assembling cars in puzzle form.

Gingerbread Man SRC Both 6-10

Players progress along a path filled with matching pieces of various parts of a gingerbread house. Pieces are accumulated to build the house.

NAME OF TOY	MANUFACTURER	INTEREST	
		Sex	*Age*

Dolls — Many — Girls — 3-12

Dress and undress dolls and encourage imaginary play. **Note:** Doll play is adaptable to almost any level of functioning.

Action Soldier—G. I. Joe — HCM — Both — 5-8

Ten-inch male doll has numerous outfits for dressing. Play equipment lends to action play.

Paper Dolls — MBC — Girls — 5-12

For the young child, start with large dolls and uncomplicated clothes to be cut out.

Fiberboard Inlay Puzzles — SIF — Both — 3-8

Four puzzles per box. Each puzzle contains twenty to forty pieces—none are interchangeable.

Fun Cards — PAR — Both — 3-5

Child must fit die-cut animals and letters, spelling their name into large individual board.

Activity Travel Kit — MBC — Both — 4-12

Includes games, puzzles, mazes, doodles.

Make-It-Box — MBC — Both — 4-10

Variety of activities (e.g. make three dimensional objects, mobiles). Stencils, crayons, and paints are supplied.

Fit-A-Square — CCE — Both — 2-4

Teaches child colors and form association by providing him with sixteen cutout rubber discs into which forty-eight pieces in twelve different shapes fit.

NAME OF TOY	MANUFACTURER	INTEREST	
		Sex	*Age*

Judgments and Readiness CPT Both 4-8

Colored rubber squares, circles, and triangles are composed of five or more concentric outlines which can be taken apart and fit together to make a solid figure.

Super Puzzle SGH Both 7+

Sixty silhouette puzzles to be solved using plastic shapes. Instruction book and solutions included.

Hex SGH Both 4-8

Eighty hexagon printed cards are matched according to color and design to form flowers.

Mr. Potato Head IICM Both 5-8

Four plastic vegetable heads and sixty pieces for creating facial and body parts.

Tinker Toys Many Both 3-8

Assorted wooden Tinker Toy pieces and moving parts used for construction.

Hammer and Nail Set CCE Both 4-6

Set includes a board, hammer, object blocks, nails, and sticks to be used in creating pictures on a wallboard.

Hammer and Nail Set HAL Both 4-7

Pounding board 12" by 10". Colored heads of Huck, Yogi, et cetera in chipboard; laying sticks, nails, and hammer are used to create humorous scenes.

Colorforms CCE Both 4-7

Make designs with die-cut plastic shapes which adhere to a plastic workboard.

NAME OF TOY	MANUFACTURER	INTEREST	
		Sex	*Age*

**Magnetic Board and Wooden
  Forms**   MCI   Both   4-7
Wooden cutouts are pieced to form a variety of characters.

Lincoln Logs   PMC   Both   4-8
                        HAL   Both   4-8
Three-quarter-inch hardwood logs and other material for construction of buildings.

Miniature Set-Up Kits   MCI   Both   4-6
Wooden cutouts can be put together to form multiple familiar scenes such as schoolrooms, farm, airport.

Flexagons   CCE   Both   5-8
Four cardboard squares and triangles assemble with rubber bands to form 3-D boats, houses, and geometric forms.

Color-In Drawing Sets   LAK   Both   4-8
Lock-in-place drawing guides help children draw predetermined pictures which are colored by number.

Rap-A-Tap Metalcraft Set   RBI   Boys   10+
Six designed metal plaques and tapping tools for making bookends and pictures.

Woodcraft Set   RBI   Boys   8-14
Six designed plywood plaques and tools for wood carving and wood painting.

**Museum Collage and
  Construction Sets**   CPT   Both   4+
A collection of various materials (e.g. faille, cork, sponge, yarn, beads) for creating a collage.

NAME OF TOY	MANUFACTURER	INTEREST *Sex*	*Age*

Fiesta Jewelled Applique Set   RBI   **Girls**   **8-14**
Six colored felt cutout appliques ready for mounting with colored nail heads. Includes instruction sheet with suggestions.

Greeting Cards   BSC   **Girls**   **5-8**
Gummed shapes to make greeting cards for all occasions.

Creating With Wood   Many   **Boys**   **5+**
Use tools and a pattern to make simple objects (e.g. go-carts, simple furniture).

Mary Poppins Paint and
  Crayon Set   HCM   **Both**   **5-8**
Presketched pictures to paint or color with painting hints included.

Color-A-Long Book   WAC   **Both**   **5-8**
Forty-five inches of running pictures to color and recolor. Surface can be wiped off again and again.

Silk Screen Set   CPT   **Girls**   **10+**
All necessary equipment and instructions are included for creating greeting cards, stationery, placemats, et cetera.

Three-Dimensional Pencil
  By Number   HCM   **Both**   **5-10**
3-D pictures of familiar television characters and shows to be completed with pencil crayons.

Stardust   HCM   **Both**   **8-15**
Similar to painting by number, but stardust and feathers are used to fill in the numbered sections. The finished picture looks like velvet.

NAME OF TOY	MANUFACTURER	INTEREST Sex	Age

Sand Art Drawing Set RBI Both 10+
Contains twelve picture cards, colored sand, sand pen, and glue.

Loom Craft HCM Girls 5-12
Various-size looms and cotton loopers to weave to make pot holders. Designs can be copied or created.

Basket Making SGH Girls 5-8
Includes precut sticks and paper strips with instructions for making six baskets.

Raffia Baskets SGH Girls 6-9
Includes four colored basket shapes and raffia for weaving.

Weave-A-Basket SGH Girls 6-10
Five baskets can be made out of basic shapes and plastic strips.

Mat Weaving SGH Girls 8-14
Six mats can be made using a ring loom and raffia.

Deluxe Magic Designer CPT Both 8+
Adjustable arms act as a guide for pen in creating and copying designs on circular sheets of paper.

Ceramic Tiles Many Both 8+
Decorate precut forms such as dishes and ash trays with tiles held together by grout.

Sewing Machine Set HCM Girls 5-8
Sets include miniature machine that operates by hand. Needles, thread, thimble, scissors, patterns, and material are furnished.

NAME OF TOY	MANUFACTURER	INTEREST	
		Sex	*Age*

Sketch-A-Bets SIF Both 4-7

Puzzles which teach numbers and letters. Child puts pegs into holes next to markings. Then he twists a white cord around the pegs following the proper order.

Picture Beads HAL Both 4-10

Small beads push into white Styrofoam to create pictures from a design sheet.

Pompon Pets SGH Girls 8-12

Miniature pets can be made out of yarn with the help of forms. Comes with complete instructions and all necessary equipment.

Jewelry Craft Assortment HCM Girls 7-10

Four different sets—charms and chains, snap-in beads, Indian beads, and stone bracelets—all for creating your own jewelry.

Hammer-Nail Design Board Set CPT Both 5-10

Two hundred varied die-cut steel shapes. Hammer and nails are used to construct designs on wallboards.

Pegboard Playtiles HAL Both 5-10

A total of 448 plastic tiles in three different shapes fit snugly into pegboard to create mosaic designs and pictures.

Plaquette-Mosaic Wall Hanging GCC Girls 8-14

Make picture wall hangings using precut mosaic shapes and glue.

Military Construction Sets HCM Boys 5-8

Interlocking plastic parts build bridges, observation towers, et cetera.

| NAME OF TOY | MANUFACTURER | INTEREST | |
		Sex	*Age*

Bolts and Nuts Builder   KOH   Both   4-6

Large wooden and plastic bolts, nuts, wheels, and other parts can be combined to form movable toys.

Inventatoy   CPT   Both   4-8

Dowels and connector parts can be manipulated to form toys with movable parts.

Wooden Plane   MCI   Both   3-8

Forty-three wooden pieces including nuts, bolts, and connectors which can be used for construction of many objects.

Bolt-It   CPT   Both   4-8

Large wooden, plastic, and metal parts to make rolling and stationary toys from suggested designs.

Hardwood Construction Set   MCI   Both   3-7

Fifty building parts—nuts, bolts, screws, drilled strips, pulleys, and four rubber tires. Wooden wrench, screwdriver, and guide booklet provided.

Funblocks   SIF   Both   4-12

Plastic interlocking blocks shaped like snowflakes. The set includes closed links, open links, corners, et cetera for endless combinations.

Take-Apart Truck and Kiddie Car   PMC   Both   4-6

Two over-sized vehicles which children take apart, put together, and ride. Has wooden nuts, bolts, a wrench, and a screwdriver.

Krupferli   CPT   Both   4-8

Plastic components for making chains, shapes, baskets, and geometric forms.

NAME OF TOY	MANUFACTURER	INTEREST	
		Sex	*Age*

Fun Time Clock WAC Both 4-7

Hands, gears, and other parts can be taken apart and put back together.

Rig-A-Jig CCE Both 5-7

Colorful plastic pieces interlock to form people, animals, trucks, and geometric forms.

See-Ques CPT Both 4-7

1. **Junior**—Nursery rhymes. Nature stories
2. **Advanced**—Many stories.

Child arranges picture cards in sequence and recreates story verbally.

Picture Sequence Cards MBC Both 5-8

Child must place picture cards in the correct order to tell the story. Twenty different stories are included.

What's Missing? Story Cards MBC Both 5-8

The child must select the missing part, to complete the picture. The pictures are labeled.

Operation MBC Both 6+

Pick-up cards determine the type of operation the player must make on a plastic man with removable plastic parts. The part must be removed carefully with a tweezer in order to score points.

Flower Craft BSC Girls 5-8

Make your own floral arrangements. Flower parts are provided with complete instructions.

Flower Basket SGH Girls 6-10

A tray full of plastic flower parts to make floral decoration. Plastic baskets and weaving material are provided.

NAME OF TOY	MANUFACTURER	INTEREST	
		Sex	*Age*

Paint By Number HCM Both 5-8
Numbered pictures of television characters (e.g. Flipper, Bambi) and water colors.

Paint By Number Books WPC Both 6-10
Paint with water colors following number instructions.

Paint By Number—Oil Paints HCM Both 6-10
Presketched, numbered pictures of familiar television stars.

Table Mat Printing SGH Girls 6-10
Nine coasters printed with outline designs ready for painting. All necessary equipment supplied.

Table Mat Stenciling SGH Girls 8-14
Seven coasters on which water resistant pictures are painted with the aid of stencils.

Burn 'N' Stain RBI Boys 10+
Wooden plaques to be burned and stained by number.

Burn-Rite Woodburning Sets RBI Boys 10+
Wooden plaques, coasters, bookends, et cetera designed for woodburning.

Lego System Blocks CCE Both 4-8
Interlocking blocks of different shapes and primary colors can be combined to form sturdy structures.

Kinder Suburbia SIF Both 4-8
Block city in which child decides the number of stories, types of buildings, pitch of the roof, and location on imaginary streets.

NAME OF TOY	MANUFACTURER	INTEREST Sex	Age

Block City CCE Both 4-8

These sets supply plastic interlocking blocks cut for building houses, stores, and buildings.

Multi-Puzzle SGH Both 6-14

Forty-two plastic parts can be fit together into forty-eight different puzzles.

Constructioneer HAL Both 5-8

Interlocking plastic blocks in a multitude of different shapes are used to build complicated objects.

American Plastic Bricks HAL Both 5-8

Interlocking plastic bricks can be used to create many different objects.

Asymmetric Space Construction CPT Both 4-8

Sixty pieces of various-sized rods and dowels for construction of various objects.

Magnasticks CCE Both 5-7

Magnetic plates hold metal construction parts together while building structures.

Snap-Eze Playforms CCE Both 5-7

A collection of unbreakable plastic rods, wheels, and blocks all interlocking to build a wide range of objects (e.g. people, houses, cars).

Woodcraft Parts, Senior Set CPT Boys 6-12

An assortment of wooden handles, spools, wheels, and balls which can be combined in various ways with the aid of nails.

| NAME OF TOY | MANUFACTURER | INTEREST | |
		Sex	*Age*

Constructo Straws   PAR   Both   6-10
Two hundred flexible plastic straws can be joined to make large-scale models.

Bend 'N' Build Construction Set   CCE   Both   6-10
Big unbreakable plastic tubes for construction of large-scale models. Connectors link tubes, and parts are movable.

Geodestix Construction Kit   CPT   Both   6-12
Sturdy rods and plastic connector joints can be manipulated to form interesting 3-D designs.

Building Models   Many   Boys   6-14
Precut plastic or wooden parts must be glued together following a pattern to make objects such as cars, boats, and planes.

Dial 'N' Spell   MBC   Both   4-8
A telephone dial on cards. Child spells words by dialing and when spelled correctly arrow points to the object.

Learn-to-Write Letter Cards   MBC   Both   6-10
Reusable cards on which the child traces printed letters with crayons. Manuscript and cursive letters are included.

Lithography Kit   CPT   Both   12+
Materials are provided for children to learn how to print cards, pictures, et cetera.

Indian Bead Craft   WAL   Both   8-14
Decorate belts, moccasins, and other precut leather objects with Indian beads. Involves stringing beads into a design.

NAME OF TOY	MANUFACTURER	INTEREST	
		Sex	*Age*

String Figures — CPT — Both — 10+
An instruction booklet tells how to create 105 designs out of string.

Paint By Number — Many — Both — 10+
Intricate pictures to oil paint by number. **Note:** At this level the paint-by-number kit would be quite complex.

Mary Poppins Needlepoint Set — HCM — Girls — 6-10
Tapestry, yarn, and needle are supplied. Finished product can be framed.

Woolly Pictures — SGH — Girls — 8-12
Six framed pictures are to be stitched to make miniature tapestries. Needles, wool, and guide sheet are supplied.

Ship in Bottle — CPT — Boys — 8-12
Child must glue precut parts of a boat and place in bottle, which is then glued together.

Paper Plays — CPT — Both — 8-12
Patterned paper is folded and cut to form 3-D sculptures.

Junior Clockmaker Kit — RBI — Boys — 10+
Put a real cuckoo clock together and make it run.

Electrical Invention Box — CPT — Boys — 6-10
Contains twenty-six pieces: light bulb, sockets, switches, bell, buzzer, et cetera which are operated by a harmless six-volt battery.

NAME OF TOY	MANUFACTURER	INTEREST *Sex*	*Age*

Electrical Invention Box   CPT   Boys   6-12

Kit includes wire, bulbs, sockets, switches, buzzers, motors. No instructions are included, to encourage the child to experiment.

Junior Electro-Experimental Set   RBI   Boys   10-16

Child learns the principle of electricity by putting together simple, safe, everyday components.

Erector Set   GIL   Boys   8+

A variety of metal building components and an electric motor for building structures.

Weaving Loom   SGH   Both   10+

Children can make scarves, mats, et cetera on miniature looms. Comes with instructions for designing articles.

Sewing   Many   Girls   10+

Sewing by hand or with the aid of a machine, using regular patterns and various types of materials.

Knitting   Many   Girls   10+

Knitting with various regulation-size needles, using different weight yarns and following a pattern.

Troke   SRC   Both   8+

A strategy game combining the skills of checkers and chess. Interlocking towers, walls, and moats are maneuvered across a board to be assembled on the goal line.

Tangle   SRC   Both   8+

Players use geometric shapes which are moved across a board to form a pattern and block the opponent's pattern.

NAME OF TOY	MANUFACTURER	INTEREST	
		Sex	*Age*

Spellit   **CAD**   **Both**   **4-8**

A dial in the center spells, adds, and subtracts. If players make the correct move, the correct picture appears in the center of the dial.

Key-Kit Spelling   **SHI**   **Both**   **4-7**

Colorful picture cards with alphabet letters to spell the name of the object. Key-cards are notched so that only the correct letters fit. A coloring workbook is included.

Key-Kit Spelling   **SHI**   **Both**   **5-8**

Colorful picture cards with alphabet letters to spell the name of the object. Key-cards are notched so that only the correct letters fit. A coloring workbook is included.

Key-Kit Arithmetic   **SHI**   **Both**   **4-7**

Colorful picture cards are notched so that only the correct number fits, to teach basic number concepts. A coloring workbook is included.

Key-Kit Arithmetic   **SHI**   **Both**   **5-8**

Colorful picture cards are notched so that only the correct number fits, to teach basic number concepts. A coloring workbook is included.

Dial Speller   **HAR**   **Both**   **6-10**

Learn to spell by association with picture and alphabet dials. Chalk, eraser, and blackboard included. Spell the word and write the word.

Kalah   **KAL**   **Both**   **6+**

This table game requires strategy, planning, quick counting, and computation.

NAME OF TOY	MANUFACTURER	INTEREST	
		Sex	*Age*

Educational Password Game   MBC   Both   10+

Players must guess words from clues (antonyms, synonyms, and word association).

Scrabble for Juniors   SRC   Both   6-12

A word and picture version of the Scrabble game. Players draw letters which are combined to form words. One side of the board has an easy pictorial version and the other side has a more advanced version.

Spill and Spell   CCE   Both   6+

Fifteen cubes used to spell words.

**Beginning Consonant
Poster Cards**   MBC   Both   6-10

Cards have a picture and a word with one or two missing letters. The child must identify the missing letters and pronounce the word.

Vowel-Links Poster Cards   MBC   Both   6-10

Cards have pictures and words with one or two missing letters. The child must insert the missing letters and pronounce the word.

Sentence Builder   MBC   Both   6-10

Alphabet letters and basic words, to build words and sentences.

Scrabble   SRC   Both   6+

A crossword game. Players draw letters which must be combined to form words appropriate for the spaces on the board.

Phonetic Word Builder   MBC   Both   7-12

Build words, using individual cards with consonants, consonant blends, special blends, double vowels, and short and long vowel endings.

NAME OF TOY	MANUFACTURER	INTEREST	
		Sex	*Age*

Arithmetic Quizmo   MBC   Both   7-12
Played similar to Lotto. Practice in addition, subtraction, multiplication, and division.

Take 12   PAR   Both   8+
Played similar to Lotto. Practice in addition, subtraction, combinations of twelve white cubes.

Numble   CPT   Both   9+
Game is similar to Scrabble. One builds number sequences that total a given amount and are divisible by a certain number.

The Winning Touch   EFG   Both   9+
The game is played like Scrabble but teaches multiplication.

Bangaroo   AMS   Both   8+
A plastic spinner propels balls into scoring pockets, resulting in the acquisition of letters. These are used to spell words.

Keyword   PAR   Both   8+
This is a crossword game.

Perquackey   LAK   Both   8+
A word game played with alphabet dice.

Dig   PAR   Both   8+
Players scoop out letters and form words of the subject named on the cards.

Probe   PAR   Both   8+
Each player conceals a secret word which others must try to guess by probing for the letters.

| NAME OF TOY | MANUFACTURER | INTEREST | |
| | | *Sex* | *Age* |

Facts-In-Five   **AIC**   **Both**   **9+**

Players are assigned five letters and five categories of subject matter. How many words or names can you come up with that start with the assigned letter and fit the classification?

Concentration   **MBC**   **Both**   **10+**

Players move numbered slides to find matching gift cards. As matches are made, more of the puzzle is revealed on the board. The first to solve the puzzle wins.

SPATIAL RELATIONS

There are two necessary perceptual skills involved in the determination of the position of an object in space. The first of these is binocular vision which adds the third dimension. A person who is blind in one eye can generally function well, however, by employing the second skill, the determination of distance and relationship of objects to one another, by knowledge of the normal or expected size of objects and comparison between them. This second skill is one of the principal techniques the graphic artist employs to create the illusion of depth.

The ordering of games has included consideration of the distance from the child to the object of judgment, the size of the various parts, and the possibility for self-correction without failing and without beginning a new trial. In a construction toy, for example, it is possible for the child to continuously correct his judgments. In a target game such as ringtoss each throw is complete with no ability to correct for error in spatial judgment until the next turn. In this connection, lever games occupy an intermediate position in grading skill because the aim may be maintained with correction for the next turn. Other things being equal, it is more difficult to judge spatial relations when the parts are small. For example, a child can determine the spatial relations of large blocks more readily than he can with Lincoln logs. The rapidity of necessary judgment is also a factor. For example, basketball involves extremely rapid decisions.

NAME OF TOY	MANUFACTURER	INTEREST Sex	Age
Cobbler's Bench	**PMC**	**Both**	1-2½

Bang bench with movable wooden pegs. Child uses wooden mallet for pounding.

Alphabet Blocks	**HAL**	**Both**	2-5

One-and-one-half-inch blocks with raised, colored alphabet letters for building and to familiarize child with alphabet.

Cubical Counting Blocks	**MBC**	**Both**	3-6

Use colored blocks to develop number concepts and learn colors while building objects.

Blocks	**PMC**	**Both**	1½-8

Colored and plain wooden blocks of varied shapes and sizes for building.

Bags of Blocks	**HAL**	**Both**	2-5

Colored and natural finish ⅞" scale wood blocks in ten different shapes.

Educational Blocks	**FPT**	**Both**	2-5

Varied-shaped wooden blocks for building.

Sculpey Polyform	**PLY**	**Both**	3+

Plastic modeling material does not harden in the air, but hardens when baked in home oven. Objects can be carved and painted.

NAME OF TOY	MANUFACTURER	INTEREST	
		Sex	*Age*

Clay   MBC   Both   3+
   1. **Clayrite**
   2. **Tru-Model**
Artificial clay used to create objects. May be reused again
and again.

Clay Modeling   CPT   Both   3+
   1. **Playdough or artificial clay**
   2. **Modo clay**—hardens without firing
   3. **Cera clay**—oven fire at home
   4. **Pottery clay**—must be fired at high temperatures
Objects can be painted or glazed.

Hi-Low Interlocking Blocks   HAL   Both   1½-4
Indented alphabet letters on 1½" blocks that interlock for
ease in building.

Stacking Ring Set   HCM   Both   1½-3
Four different-size rings fit on a wooden peg.

Giant Rack-A-Stack   FPT   Both   1-3
Ten rings fit on a cane in size sequence.

Poly Blocks and Rods   PMC   Both   2-5
Large plastic blocks in three shapes to fit over ⅝" dowels.

Creative Blocks   FPT   Both   1-4
Plastic blocks fit over wooden dowels.

Nuts and Bolts   HCM   Both   1½-3
Sturdy plastic threaded bolt serves as base on which to fit
four large nuts.

| NAME OF TOY | MANUFACTURER | INTEREST | |
		Sex	Age

Nuts and Bolts CCE Both 2-4
  Nuts and bolts made of plastic must be matched for size
  and color.

Sandbox Play Many Both 2-5
  Give the child different-sized bottles, cans, jars, funnels, pans,
  sieves for filling and dumping the sand.

Clothespin Dairy Wagon PMC Both 1½-3
  Push-pull toy has two small plastic milk bottles on wooden
  milk truck. Six colorful clothespins to drop into bottles. Truck
  makes a motor sound when pulled.

Fill 'N' Dump Bottle CCE Both 2-4
  Quart plastic bottles with spools and clothespins

Nesting Toys PMC Both 1-3
  1. Nesting Bowls
  2. Billy and His Barrels
  3. Building Cups
  4. Stacking Pyramid
  5. Nesting Nuts and Bolts

Stacking Toys MCI Both 2-4
  An elephant, an owl, and a Mexican man made of several
  wooden pieces which are stacked in a precise order.

Nesting Blocks MCI Both 3-5
  Wooden stacking blocks with pictures painted on the sides.

The Chicken In The Eggs PMC Both 3-6
  Six plastic eggs, graduated in size, are taken apart to find
  the chick.

NAME OF TOY	MANUFACTURER	INTEREST	
		Sex	*Age*

Beads For Stringing   MBC   Both   2-6
Different shapes, sizes, and colors.

Indian Beads   PMC   Both   2-4
Large beads for stringing.

Mini Pop-up Model Books   MCI   Both   1½-4
These books pop up in 3-D scenes of familiar settings (e.g. railroad station, airport). **Note:** The pop-up book type of toy is rather passive with little active play value. It does abstract spatial relations, however, and may illustrate useful principles to the child.

Mini Pop-up Books   MCI   Both   1½-4
These books open up to show a 3-D illustrated story in full color.

Panascopic Model Books   MCI   Both   1½-6
These books unfold into 3-D scenes which are accompanied by a story. They cover subjects such as circus life, Indian camp, and jungle.

Notchies   CPT   Both   3-5
Large plastic blocks interlock in various positions to assist the child in building precarious forms.

Interslot   MCI   Both   4-8
Thirty-four wooden pieces in six different shapes can be fit together to create structures.

Bag of Blocks and Rods   HAL   Both   3-5
Wooden ⅞" building blocks in eleven different shapes; ½" diameter wooden rods are used to attach blocks.

NAME OF TOY	MANUFACTURER	INTEREST	
		Sex	*Age*

Busy Board   BSC   Both   2-5
Wooden board with bolts, nuts, hinges with which children can experiment.

Lacing Boot   CPT   Both   3-5
Wooden boot and heavy shoelace for lacing.

Tinker Box   CHI   Both   2-4
Plastic tool box into which large screws, nuts, and bolts can be put with the aid of a plastic hammer, screwdriver, and wrench.

Workbench   PMC   Both   3-5
A wooden bench with wooden nuts, bolts, screws, and nails which can be manipulated.

Skaneatles Transportation Sets   PMC   Both   2-10
Wooden railroad sets—tracks, cars, et cetera.

New Tot Railroad   PMC   Both   2-9
Twenty-eight piece plastic railroad set for beginners. Child builds in many ways.

Toy Ironing Board and Iron   SIF   Girls   4-7
Girls can practice ironing their doll clothes.

All By Himself—Book   CPT   Both   3-5
Cloth book with washable objects to teach child to dress himself—button, snap, tie, and zip.

Make-It-Box   MBC   Both   4-10
Variety of activities (e.g. make 3-D objects, mobiles). Stencils, crayons, and paints are supplied.

NAME OF TOY	MANUFACTURER	INTEREST	
		Sex	*Age*

Junior Workshop   HAR   Both   3-5

Four plastic tools and nails to use with plastic lumber.

Mr. Builder's Home Workshop   HAR   Both   3-5

Ten plastic tools, nails, and lumber for construction.

Magnetic Construction Set   BSC   Both   2-6

Horseshoe magnet, a number of disc and bar magnets, and various-shaped metal pieces for constructing objects.

Landscape Peg Set   PMC   Both   2½-6

Child constructs landscapes with pegs and wooden shapes.

Peg Desk   PMC   Both   3-8

Desk with attached seat. Top of desk is a blackboard. Chalk and eraser are supplied. Under the top is a pegboard. Pegs are supplied.

Comic Corner   CCE   Both   3-5

Thirty-four interchangeable pegged parts to make your own street scenes. People, traffic light, and store parts are included.

Giant Snap-Lock Ring and Beads   FPT   Both   2-4

Colored plastic parts snap together to make chains and other objects.

Snap 'N' Play   SIF   Both   4-7

Wooden pieces of various shapes and sizes snap together to make objects.

Rubber Beaded Pegboards   CPT   Both   4-8

Duplicate or make designs with pegs on the board.

NAME OF TOY	MANUFACTURER	INTEREST	
		Sex	*Age*

Miniature Series   MCI   Both   1½-4

Vivid picture stories of familiar subject matter such as shopping, the farm, the zoo in 3-D.

Miniature Set-Up Kits   MCI   Both   4-6

Wooden cutouts can be put together to form multiple familiar scenes such as schoolrooms, farm, airport.

Construction Kit   MCI   Both   3-5

Nuts, bolts, and connectors (wooden) are joined to form objects and toys.

Wood Toy Builder   PMC   Both   3-8

Construction kit consists of wooden girders, nuts, bolts, screws, and appropriate plastic tools.

Children's Hour   PAR   Both   4-8

Three games in one: Peanut the Elephant, Porky the Pig, and ABC Fishing.

Magnetic Fish Pond   SGH   Both   4-8

The challenge of outdoor fishing at home. Ten plastic fish, four rods with magnets, and colorful pond are provided.

Barrel of Monkeys   LAK   Both   4-8

The object is to use one plastic monkey to hook another from the barrel to form a long chain.

Loony Links   AMS   Both   5-8

Snap parts of bodies together to form animals and people.

Mix-Nix   AMS   Both   4-7

Child changes both body and facial characteristics of heavy cardboard figures by adding 3-D parts.

NAME OF TOY	MANUFACTURER	INTEREST Sex	Age

Wooden Plane   MCI   Both   3-8

Forty-three wooden pieces including nuts, bolts, and connectors which can be used for construction of many objects.

Bolt-It   CPT   Both   4-8

Large wooden, plastic, and metal parts to make rolling and stationary toys from suggested designs.

Hardwood Construction Set   MCI   Both   3-7

Fifty building parts—nuts, bolts, screws, drilled strips, pulleys, and four rubber tires. Wooden wrench, screwdriver, and guide booklet provided.

Bolts and Nuts Builder   KOH   Both   4-6

Large wooden and plastic bolts, nuts, wheels, and other parts can be combined to form movable toys.

Take-Apart Truck and Kiddie Car   PMC   Both   4-6

Two over-sized vehicles which children take apart, put together, and ride. Has wooden nuts, bolts, a wrench, and a screwdriver.

Fun Time Clock   WAC   Both   4-7

Hands, gears, and other parts can be taken apart and put back together.

Inventatoy   CPT   Both   4-8

Dowels and connector parts can be manipulated to form toys with movable parts.

Electric Train Sets   Many   Boys   5+

This category covers a variety of electric trains. **Note:** Electric train arrangements may be simple or quite complex with respect to spatial arrangements.

NAME OF TOY	MANUFACTURER	INTEREST	
		Sex	*Age*

Snap-Eze Playforms CCE Both 5-7

A collection of unbreakable plastic rods, wheels, and blocks all interlocking to build a wide range of objects (e.g. people, houses, cars).

Knitting Ring SGH Girls 6-10

Knit with the assistance of a frame. Practice wool and colored illustrations are supplied.

My Knitting Set PAR Girls 6-12

Learn to knit with the aid of a special tool.

**Mary Poppins Giant
Knitting Spool** HCM Girls 6-10

Make many useful items from this kit. All necessary materials included as well as instruction book.

Knitting Nancy SGH Girls 8-10

Knit long strands with the aid of a wooden frame. These strands can be combined to make mats, rugs, et cetera.

Loom Craft HCM Girls 5-12

Various-sized looms and cotton loopers to weave to make pot holders. Designs can be copied or created.

Braiding Many Both 5-12

Braid simple lanyards out of colored laces.

Basket Making SGH Girls 5-8

Includes precut sticks and paper strips with instructions for making six baskets.

Raffia Baskets SGH Girls 6-9

Includes four colored basket shapes and raffia for weaving.

NAME OF TOY	MANUFACTURER	INTEREST	
		Sex	*Age*

Weave-A-Basket   SGH   Girls   6-10
Five baskets can be made out of basic shapes and plastic strips.

Mat Weaving   SGH   Girls   8-14
Six mats can be made using a ring loom and raffia.

Magnasticks   CCE   Both   5-7
Magnetic plates hold metal construction parts together while building structures.

Funblocks   SIF   Both   4-12
Plastic interlocking blocks shaped like snowflakes. The set includes closed links, open links, corners, et cetera for endless combinations.

Flexagons   CCE   Both   5-8
Four cardboard squares and triangles assemble with rubber bands to form 3-D boats, houses, and geometric forms.

Military Construction Sets   HCM   Boys   5-8
Interlocking plastic parts build bridges, observation towers, et cetera.

Flower Basket   SGH   Girls   6-10
A tray full of plastic flower parts to make floral decorations. Plastic baskets and weaving material are provided.

Flower Craft   BSC   Girls   5-8
Make your own floral arrangements. Flower parts are provided with complete instructions.

Building Models   Many   Boys   6-14
Precut plastic or wooden parts must be glued together following a pattern to make objects such as cars, boats, and planes.

NAME OF TOY	MANUFACTURER	INTEREST	
		Sex	*Age*

Lincoln Logs   PMC   Both   4-8

                           HAL   Both   4-8

Three-quarter-inch hardwood logs and other material for construction of buildings.

Asymmetric Space Construction   CPT   Both   4-8

Sixty pieces of various-sized rods and dowels for construction of various objects.

Electrical Invention Box   CPT   Boys   6-10

Contains twenty-six pieces: light bulb, sockets, switches, bell, buzzer, et cetera, which are operated by a harmless six-volt battery.

Electrical Invention Box   CPT   Boys   6-12

Kit includes wire, bulbs, sockets, switches, buzzers, motors, et cetera. No instructions are included, to encourage the child to experiment.

Junior Electro-Experimental Set   RBI   Boys   10-16

Child learns the principle of electricity by putting together simple, safe, everyday components.

Punching Bag On A Stand   Many   Boys   5+

Child punches at a bag.

Bill Ding   SIF   Both   4-10

Wooden clowns can be manipulated to perform thousands of balancing acts on wooden rods.

Jumbo Tiddledy Winks   MBC   Both   6-12

Child uses large winks to pop smaller winks into a cup in the center of the playing board.

NAME OF TOY	MANUFACTURER	INTEREST	
		Sex	*Age*

Tiddly Turtle   AMS   Both   5-10
Tiddly Winks in a new action game. The object is to snap winks into a turtle back and advance your turtle toward the finish line.

Tiddly Winks   MCI   Both   5-10
                              FAR   Both   5-10
Plastic winks are used to pop each other into the mushroom-shaped wooden target.

Flips   SGH   Both   6-12
Similar to Tiddly Winks. The plastic dots must be flipped into the target cup.

Drag Strip   MBC   Both   5-12
Players propel race cars down drag strips with marbles.

Top Shuffle Board   PAR   Both   6+
A miniature shuffleboard game. Players use a spinning top to guide discs.

Top Ten Pins   PAR   Both   6+
Miniature bowling. A spinning top knocks down small plastic pins.

Ring Toss   MBC   Both   3-8
Wooden-base target at which rope rings are tossed.

Ring Toss   HAR   Both   4-8
Four large plastic rings to be tossed at a target peg on a stand.

Deluxe Horseshoe Set   HAR   Both   3-8
Four plastic horseshoes to be tossed at a peg target on a stand.

NAME OF TOY	MANUFACTURER	INTEREST	
		Sex	*Age*

Clown Bean Bag   PAR   Both   5-10

Child tosses bean bags into holes in a stand-up target.

Bean Bags and Board   CPT   Both   5-10

Board with easel stand has five target holes of different sizes and shapes through which bean bags must be thrown.

Hopscotch   CPT   Girls   5-12

A portable playing surface which can be used inside. One hops from square to square.

Twister   MBC   Both   8+

Two players put all four extremities on colored circles on a plastic game rug. A spinner shows where the player must move his hands and feet next. This requires a sense of balance.

Suction Dart Game   Many   Both   4+

Games include targets and darts with suction cups.

Dart Game   Many   Both   4+

This game can be played with hand darts or dart gun. Child throws or shoots darts at a target.

Target Games Assortment   HCM   Both   5+

Three different metal targets with three rubber suction darts.

Shoot 'Em Down Soldier Set   HAR   Both   3-6

Ten plastic soldiers on a rack. The object is to shoot them down with corks ejected from toy cannons attached to a lever.

Krupferli   CPT   Both   4-8

Plastic components for making chains, shapes, baskets, and geometric forms.

NAME OF TOY	MANUFACTURER	INTEREST	
		Sex	Age

Constructioneer   HAL   Both   5-8

Interlocking plastic blocks in a multitude of different shapes are used to build complicated objects.

Tinker Toys   Many   Both   3-8

Assorted wooden Tinker Toy pieces and moving parts used for construction.

Lego System Blocks   CCE   Both   4-8

Interlocking blocks of different shapes and primary colors can be combined to form sturdy structures.

American Plastic Bricks   HAL   Both   5-8

Interlocking plastic bricks can be used to create many different objects.

Block City   CCE   Both   5-8

These sets supply plastic interlocking blocks cut for building houses, stores, and buildings.

Kinder Suburbia   SIF   Both   4-8

Block city in which child decides the number of stories, types of buildings, pitch of the roof, and location on imaginary streets.

Rig-A-Jig   CCE   Both   5-7

Colorful plastic pieces interlock to form people, animals, trucks, and geometric forms.

Sharp Shooter   CAD   Both   5-10

A target game. Players use a plastic pistol and rubber-band ammunition to shoot at mounted targets.

NAME OF TOY	MANUFACTURER	INTEREST	
		Sex	*Age*

Flippo AMS Both 5-10

Marbles are flipped at targets in the center of the board by aiming a plastic basket attached to a lever.

Pow! The Cannon Game MBC Both 5-12

Players fire at each others' standing army by pulling the lever of a cannon loaded with marbles.

Wow! Pillow Fight Game MBC Girls 5-12

Players attempt to knock down their opponents' men with plastic pillows ejected from miniature beds operated by a lever.

Zing-A-Ring AMS Both 5-8

Six plastic rings are shot from a spring-action gun at a desired target.

Tic-Tac-Toe Target Game CAD Both 5-10

The object is to shoot a plastic ball at pails on the inclined 3-D target by pulling a lever.

Shoot-Out MBC Both 5-12

Shoot at targets on small plastic board.

Shootin Gallery Set MTI Boys 6-10

Includes toy Winchester and pistol, plastic bullets, caps, and target.

Shenanigans MBC Both 5-12

This is a real carnival—3-D game. Players move on a board and test their skill at miniature carnival games.

NAME OF TOY	MANUFACTURER	INTEREST	
		Sex	*Age*

Flying Hats   SGH   Both   6-14

Plastic hats are flipped at a target by pulling levers. Score varies with ability to hit certain areas on the target.

Are You On The Ball?   MBC   Both   8+

Players must guide ten steel balls into a center hole by pulling action levers. A scoring slot records the player's skill.

Bowling Game   MBC   Both   4-10

Ten wooden soldiers to be bowled over by small wooden balls.

Bowl-A-Strike   HCM   Both   6+

Regulation-size plastic pins and ball.

Bowling Set   CPT   Both   6-12

Eleven ½" unbreakable bowling pins and two large balls.

Archery   Many   Both   8+

Using a bow, shoot arrows at a target.

Shuffleboard   PAR   Both   6+

Discs are propelled toward a target with a long implement.

Croquet   Many   Both   6+

Players propel a wooden ball through wire wickets with a wooden mallet.

Stilts   Many   Both   5-10

Pair of poles fitted with a footrest somewhere along its length, used for walking.

Woodcraft Parts, Senior Set   CPT   Boys   6-12

An assortment of wooden handles, spools, wheels, and balls which can be combined in various ways with the aid of nails.

NAME OF TOY	MANUFACTURER	INTEREST	
		Sex	*Age*

Sewing Machine Set   **HCM**   **Girls**   **5-8**

Sets include miniature machine that operates by hand; needles, thread, thimble, scissors, patterns, and material are included.

Operation   **MBC**   **Both**   **6+**

Pick-up cards determine the type of operation the player must make on a plastic man with removable plastic parts. The part must be removed carefully with a tweezer in order to score points.

Booby Trap   **PAR**   **Both**   **8+**

Players score by removing plastic counters from the board. One wrong move may trigger a spring that scatters the pieces and they lose points.

Creating With Wood   **Many**   **Boys**   **5+**

Use tools and a pattern to make simple objects—(e.g. go-carts, simple furniture).

Bend 'N' Build Construction Set   **CCE**   **Both**   **6-10**

Big unbreakable plastic tubes for construction of large-scale models. Connectors link tubes and parts are movable.

Geodestix Construction Kit   **CPT**   **Both**   **6-12**

Sturdy rods and plastic connector joints can be manipulated to form interesting 3-D designs.

Constructo Straws   **PAR**   **Both**   **6-10**

Two hundred flexible plastic straws can be joined to make large-scale models.

Knot Tying Board   **CPT**   **Boys**   **10+**

Booklet, practice board, and rope to learn various methods of tying knots.

NAME OF TOY	MANUFACTURER	INTEREST	
		Sex	*Age*

Ship in Bottle   CPT   Boys   8-12

Child must glue precut parts of a boat and place in bottle, which is then glued together.

Bottlecap Baseball   AMS   Boys   6-10

Authentic plays on a 4' by 4' board utilizing bottlecaps.

Frantic Frogs   MBC   Both   5-12

Players wind plastic frogs and race on a board. Each player must be quick to direct his frog with a stick into the correct cove.

Carom Jump Ball   CAR   Both   5-10

The object is to shoot all of your table tennis balls over the net onto your opponent's side by aiming and pulling the lever. The player with the least number of balls is the winner.

Bagatelle Pin Ball   HCM   Both   6-10

Comes in three themes. Two action levers keep ball in play as long as possible to attain the highest score.

Deluxe Pool Table   HAR   Both   5-8

Two miniature spring-action cues shoot plastic balls into the pockets of a miniature pool table.

Toy Mazes   MBC   Both   6+
     1. **Skill-it Frying Pan**
     2. **Fry-it Maze**
     3. **Boob Tube**

Marble Maze Assortment   HCM   Both   5-10

The game comes in three themes. Player must skillfully guide the marble through the obstacle course from start to finish.

NAME OF TOY	MANUFACTURER	INTEREST	
		Sex	*Age*

Crazy Maze LAK Both 6-10

Players guide marbles past traps in the incline maze to the winner's gate by remote control.

Pee Wee Pool HCM Both 6-10

A swivel plunger allows you to direct your play. Marbles are shot into pockets for scores.

Nok-Hockey CAR Boys 6+

A miniature hockey game. Players hit wooden pucks with hockey sticks. The object is to get the puck into the opponent's goal.

Hockey CAD Boys 8+

Mechanical levers control puck and goalies in a miniature hockey game.

Basket CAD Boys 8+

Miniature basketball. Players operate levers which throw the ball at the basket.

Indoor Bas Bal CAD Boys 8+

A miniature action baseball game where players manipulate levers to pitch and hit balls.

Paddle-Pango AMS Both 5-10

A miniature table tennis game. Plastic balls are hit with small plastic paddles.

Labyrinth MFC Both 8+

The player guides a small steel ball through the maze by tilting the board at different angles.

NAME OF TOY	MANUFACTURER	INTEREST	
		Sex	*Age*

Pick-Up-Sticks AMS Both 5+

The object is to flip sticks off a pile without disturbing other sticks.

Double Pick-Up-Sticks PAR Both 6+

Players attempt to remove individual wooden sticks from a pile without disturbing the others.

Jack Straws PAR Both 6+

Played similar to pick-up-sticks. Players must pick up small plastic tools from a pile randomly dropped from the box.

Glassblowing Set CPT Both 16+

All equipment included for blowing your own creations.

Erector Set GIL Boys 8+

A variety of metal building components and an electric motor for building structures.

Knitting Many Girls 10+

Knitting with various regulation-size needles using different weight yarns and following a pattern.

Sewing Many Girls 10+

Sewing by hand or with the aid of a machine, using regular patterns and various types of materials.

Junior Clockmaker Kit RBI Boys 10+

Put a real cuckoo clock together and make it run.

String Figures CPT Both 10+

An instruction booklet tells how to create 105 designs out of string.

NAME OF TOY	MANUFACTURER	INTEREST	
		Sex	*Age*

Slot Cars Many Boys 6+

Miniature electric racing cars which can be controlled at a distance. Skill is required to keep them at maximum speed without leaving the track.

Jacks Many Girls 8+

The player bounces a small ball and attempts to pick up a varying number of jacks while catching the ball again.

Hooper-Dooper AMS Both 6-10

A plastic hoop adaptable for scooting, bouncing, et cetera.

Pitch Back CPT Boys 5+

This pitching device is a silent catcher which returns the ball to the player. (A net attached to a steel frame with springs.)

Flying Hats HAR Both 5-10

Three flying hats can be tossed and caught between players.

Bat and Ball Many Boys 5+

Wooden or plastic bat and ball. The object is to hit the ball with the bat when someone throws it towards you.

Jump Rope Many Girls 6-10

A piece of rope with handles attached on each end. The object is to jump over the rope as it swirls in a circle.

Wooden Hoops CCE Both 6-10

Various-sized hoops are rolled and controlled by a stick.

Toss-Up CAR Both 6+

The object is to flip a ring onto a hook attached to a rod, by springing another rod.

NAME OF TOY	MANUFACTURER	INTEREST	
		Sex	*Age*

Indian Bead Craft   WAL   Both   8-14

Decorate belts, moccasins, and other precut leather objects with Indian beads. Involves stringing beads into a design.

Weaving Loom   SGH   Both   10+

Children can make scarves, mats, et cetera on miniature looms. Comes with instructions for designing articles.

Balance Building Set   MCI   Both   5-10

Fifteen odd-shaped blocks for building towers.

Blockhead   CCE   Both   6+

Many different-shaped wooden blocks are placed one on top of another. The object is to add shapes without tumbling the structure.

Magnatel   MTI   Both   6+

Ten games in one including Krokay and Bumber Pool.

Carom   CAR   Both   6+

The object is to shoot caroms into pockets on the board with a wooden cue stick.

Junior Pocket Billiards   WAC   Both   6+

Junior version of billiards. Includes ten balls, cues, and playing surface.

Skibble   LAK   Both   6+

Players race each other around the board with round discs (skibbles) which are played off the side boards. Similar to pool.

Pegity   PAR   Both   8+

The object is to get five pegs of one color in an uninterrupted row while blocking opponents.

NAME OF TOY	MANUFACTURER	INTEREST	
		Sex	*Age*

Mandalay   **FOR**   **Both**   **10+**

The object is to rebuild the tower of discs on another needle, never placing a larger disc on a smaller disc, and moving only one disc at a time.

Kik-It   **CAR**   **Both**   **6+**

This is a soccer-hockey-basketball combination. A table tennis ball is advanced to opponent's basket by wire hoops attached to rods.

Volleyball   **Many**   **Both**   **8+**

Using hands only, hit a ball back and forth over the net. Usually involves more than two players.

Tennis   **Many**   **Both**   **7+**

Players hit a ball back and forth over a net with a racket.

Badminton   **Many**   **Both**   **7+**

Hit a birdie back and forth across a net with lightweight racket.

Shuttle Loop   **CPT**   **Both**   **7+**

Players hit a birdie through a metal hoop with wooden paddles.

Basketball   **Many**   **Both**   **8+**

Involves dribbling and shooting the ball through a net basket attached to a wire loop elevated at a prescribed height.

Takrow   **SPO**   **Both**   **7+**

A plastic ball is caught in a basket attached to a short stick and thrown to the next player.

NAME OF TOY	MANUFACTURER	INTEREST	
		Sex	*Age*

Jai-A-Lai   **Many**   **Boys**   **8+**
Using a wicker basket attached to a handle, toss and catch a small rubber ball.

Ping Pong   **PAR**   **Both**   **7+**
Players hit a plastic ball back and forth across a table net with a paddle.

Paper Plays   **CPT**   **Both**   **8-12**
Patterned paper is folded and cut to form 3-D sculptures.

Double Diabalo   **CPT**   **Both**   **9+**
Players must balance a rubber top along a string and work the string to increase the speed of the top. Top can also be thrown to the next player to catch on his string.

Juggling   **CPT**   **Both**   **10+**
Six rubber balls and step-by-step lessons on how to master this art.

Troke   **SRC**   **Both**   **8+**
A strategy game combining the skills of checkers and chess. Interlocking towers, walls, and moats are maneuvered across a board to be assembled on the goal line.

FIGURE-GROUND

To the young infant, sensory stimuli must appear as a confused mélange. As the child grows he sorts out the stimuli with the increasing realization that, at a given point in time, only some of the stimuli are relevant in dealing with the situation at hand. In the beginning, however, the child is easily distracted by extraneous stimuli in the environment. With maturity, there is increasing ability to concentrate on the relevant (the figure) and to ignore the extraneous (the ground). Impairment in this area is a severe handicap in education as it hampers the child's ability to focus attention and to follow assignments to completion.

All toys and games require the ability to perceive figure-ground distinctions just to focus on the material. The toys included in this category were selected because they more specifically require figure-ground differentiation.

NAME OF TOY	MANUFACTURER	INTEREST	
		Sex	*Age*
Miniature Series	MCI	Both	1½-4

Vivid picture stories of familiar subject matter such as shopping, the farm, the zoo in 3-D. **Note:** The earliest items listed are passive, unless the parent creates games. Learning is enhanced by involvement.

Mini Pop-up Books	MCI	Both	1½-4

These books open up to show a 3-D illustrated story in full color.

Mini Pop-up Model Books	MCI	Both	1½-4

These books pop up in 3-D scenes of familiar settings (e.g. railroad station, airport).

Rag Books	MCI	Both	1½-4

Six different picture stories with large pictures on cloth pages.

Panascopic Model Books	MCI	Both	1½-6

These books unfold into 3-D scenes which are accompanied by a story. They cover subjects such as circus life, Indian camp, and jungle.

Animal Fun	MBC	Both	3-8

Animals are fitted into appropriate jungle scenes. Letters are provided so the child can spell out the animals' names upon identification.

NAME OF TOY	MANUFACTURER	INTEREST Sex	Age
Painting	Many	Both	3+

   1. Water colors with brush
   2. Dri-mark water colors
   3. Tempera
Painting has a wide range of applicability.

Simple Things To Color	PMC	Both	4-7

Large pictures to color for young children.

Landscape Peg Set	PMC	Both	2½-6

Child constructs landscapes with pegs and wooden shapes.

Play Chest	HCM	Both	3-5

Wooden chest complete with blackboard, pegboard, mallet, and pegs.

Peg Desk	PMC	Both	3-8

Desk with attached seat. Top of desk is a blackboard. Chalk and eraser are supplied. Under the top is a pegboard. Pegs are supplied.

Rubber Beaded Pegboard	CPT	Both	4-8

Duplicate or make designs with pegs on the board.

Activity Travel Kit	MBC	Both	4-12

Includes games, puzzles, mazes, doodles. One of the items contains hidden objects in pictures.

Miniature Set-up Kits	MCI	Both	4-6

Wooden cutouts can be put together to form multiple familiar scenes such as school rooms, farm, airport.

NAME OF TOY	MANUFACTURER	INTEREST	
		Sex	*Age*

Lotto EUC Both 4-8
1. ABC Lotto
2. Zoo Lotto
3. Farm Lotto
4. The World About Us Lotto
5. What's Missing Lotto
6. Go-Together Lotto
7. Object Lotto

The child must match the picture cards to pictures on the playing boards.

Color-A-Long Book WAC Both 5-8

Forty-five inches of running pictures to color and recolor. Surface can be wiped off again and again.

Crayon Coloring Cards SGH Both 5-8

Ten stencil cards showing colors to be used, to teach the first steps in drawing. Crayons are supplied.

**Mary Poppins Paint and
Crayon Set** HCM Both 5-8

Presketched pictures to paint or color with painting hints included.

Paint By Number HCM Both 5-8

Numbered pictures of television characters (e.g. Flipper, Bambi) and water colors.

Dart Game Many Both 4+

This game can be played with hand darts or dart gun. Child throws or shoots darts at a target.

Suction Dart Game Many Both 4+

Games include targets and darts with suction cups.

NAME OF TOY	MANUFACTURER	INTEREST	
		Sex	*Age*

Target Games Assortment   HCM   Both   5+
Three different metal targets with three rubber suction darts.

Sharp Shooter   CAD   Both   5-10
A target game. Players use a plastic pistol and rubber-band ammunition to shoot at mounted targets.

Shenanigans   MBC   Both   5-12
This is a real carnival—3-D game. Players move on a board and test their skill at miniature carnival games.

Shootin Gallery Set   MTI   Boys   6-10
Includes toy Winchester and pistol, plastic bullets, caps, and target.

Archery   Many   Both   8+
Using a bow, shoot arrows at a target.

Operation   MBC   Both   6+
Pick-up cards determine the type of operation the player must make on a plastic man with removable plastic parts. The part must be removed carefully with a tweezer in order to score points.

Picture Sequence Cards   MBC   Both   5-8
Child must place picture cards in the correct order to tell the story. Twenty different stories are included.

What's Missing? Story Cards   MBC   Both   5-8
The child must select the missing part, to complete the picture. The pictures are labeled.

NAME OF TOY	MANUFACTURER	INTEREST	
		Sex	*Age*

**Three-Dimensional Pencil
By Number**   HCM   Both   5-10

3-D pictures of familiar television characters and shows to be completed with pencil crayons.

Crow   PAR   Both   4-12

A card game to play when traveling. Players match objects they see with cards. This involves the figure-ground distinction for real objects while moving.

Luggage Sewing Assortment   HCM   Girls   5-8

Three different sets—embroidery, sewing, and stitch-a-story. All necessary materials included.

Burn 'N' Stain   RBI   Boys   10+

Wooden plaques to be burned and stained by number.

Burn-Rite Woodburning Sets   RBI   Boys   10+

Wooden plaques, coasters, bookends designed for woodburning.

Copper and Metal Tooling   Many   Boys   10+

Using a design, hammer a pattern into metal plates, et cetera with various tools.

Make-It Box   MBC   Both   4-10

Variety of activities (e.g. make 3-D objects, mobiles). Stencils, crayons, and paints are supplied.

Activity Fun   WPC   Both   6-10

Soft-cover book of activities such as dot-to-dot completion of pictures, mazes, pictures to finish, and simple objects to make.

NAME OF TOY	MANUFACTURER	INTEREST	
		Sex	*Age*

Paint By Number—Oil Paints   HCM   Both   6-10
Presketched, numbered pictures of familiar television stars.

Paint By Number Books   WPC   Both   6-10
Paint with water colors following number instructions.

Woolly Pictures   SGH   Girls   8-12
Six framed pictures are to be stitched to make miniature tapestries. Needles, wool, and guide sheet are supplied.

Jack Straws   PAR   Both   6+
Played similar to pick-up-sticks. Players must pick up small plastic tools from a pile randomly dropped from the box.

Double Pick-Up-Sticks   PAR   Both   6+
Players attempt to remove individual wooden sticks from a pile without disturbing the others.

Pick-Up-Sticks   AMS   Both   5+
The object is to flip sticks off a pile without disturbing other sticks.

Plaquette-Mosaic Wall Hanging   GCC   Girls   8-14
Make picture wall hangings using precut mosaic shapes and glue.

Embroidery Set   PAR   Girls   5-8
Child decorates a prestamped doll bedspread and pillow set. All necessary material included.

Mary Poppins Needlepoint Set   HCM   Girls   6-10
Tapestry, yarn, and needle are supplied. Finished product can be framed.

NAME OF TOY	MANUFACTURER	INTEREST	
		Sex	*Age*

My Hankies — SGH — Girls — 8-12

Five colored hankies printed for cross-stitch embroidery. Yarn and frame are supplied.

Mat Embroidery — SGH — Girls — 8-12

Four colored linen mats printed with easy-to-follow designs. Yarn and frame are supplied.

Indian Bead Craft — WAL — Both — 8-14

Decorate belts, moccasins, and other precut leather objects with Indian beads. Involves stringing beads into a design.

Paint By Number — Many — Both — 10+

Intricate pictures to oil paint by number.

Knitting — Many — Girls — 10+

Knitting with various regulation-size needles using different weight yarns and following a pattern.

Weaving Loom — SGH — Both — 10+

Children can make scarves, mats, et cetera on miniature looms. Comes with instructions for designing articles.

AUDITORY PERCEPTION

M ANY OF THE GAMES listed in other categories involve some degree of verbalization among players. Even when verbalization is not essential there is an advantage in play if the child is able to perceive auditory stimuli accurately. There are very few games and toys constructed specifically for the purpose of assisting the child to develop skills in the area of auditory perception.

Much academic learning requires accurate perception of auditory stimuli. For example, the teacher gives most instructions and directions orally in the elementary grades. The child must be able to perceive the likeness and differences of the sounds by sorting, matching, and categorizing in order to comprehend the teacher's communication. The child must learn to associate certain sounds and groups of sounds with the appropriate visual stimuli. This is particularly important in learning to read. Sounds must be matched to specific written symbols or letters. Another important skill involves the child's ability to focus on the teacher's voice through all the background noises (e.g., other children's voices, voices in the street). This skill is auditory figure-ground perception. There are other skills involved in the perception of sounds; however, games included seemed to fall most comfortably into these two categories.

LIKE-DIFFERENT

NAME OF TOY	MANUFACTURER	INTEREST Sex	Age
Musical Toys	PMC	Both	1-3½

1. Fireman Xylo   3. Pound 'N' Twirl
2. Bell Stack   4. Bell Boys

Swiss Crank Box	MCI	Both	1-7

Wooden picture box with crank. It plays various tunes.

NAME OF TOY	MANUFACTURER	INTEREST	
		Sex	*Age*

Rag Books   MCI   Both   1½-4

Six different picture stories with large pictures on cloth pages.

Miniature Series   MCI   Both   1½-4

Vivid picture stories of familiar subject matter such as shopping, the farm, zoo in 3-D.

Voice Books   MCI   Both   1½-4

Each picture on the cover hides the appropriate voice, and eight illustrated pages show the object in various situations. The voice sounds when the child touches the cover.

Barnyard Voices   MCI   Both   2-5

Wooden cylinders which can be tipped to produce an animal sound. Pictures are painted on the outside.

Musical Instruments   Many   Both   3+

     1. Drums   5. Recorder
     2. Whistle   6. Tonette
     3. Bells   7. Maracas
     4. Xylophone   8. Guitar

Headstart With Music   CPT   Both   3-8

Two 12" LP records and an accompanying twenty-eight page book help to introduce children to listening and singing skills.

Muffin In The City   YPR   Both   4-8
Muffin In The Country   YPR   Both   4-8

A record about a dog who visits a big city and the country. The many sounds of the city and country are identified.

Home Movie Sound Effects   CPT   Both   4+

The record of forty-two different sound effects can be adapted for many uses. It can be used with a small child to develop listening skills.

| NAME OF TOY | MANUFACTURER | INTEREST | |
		Sex	*Age*
Color Bingo	EUC	Both	5-8

Teaches color and number identification.

Bingo	SRC	Both	6+
	MBC	Both	6+
	FAR	Both	6+

The original Bingo game where the caller calls the numbers and players cover the numbers in an attempt to get a Bingo.

| **Go Fish** | Many | Both | 5-8 |

Played with a regular deck of cards. Each player requests a number from the other players.

| **Batta Hai** | CAD | Both | 6+ |

This game combines the simplicity of Lotto with the elements of strategy. Each player has a board and matches cards called by another player. Cards have faces, numbers, and domino matchings.

| **Smarty** | EFG | Both | 7-12 |

Arithmetic-Bingo game which teaches addition and subtraction.

| **Phonetic Quizmo** | MBC | Both | 6-8 |

Parent says sound; child finds letter or letters on card. Similar to Lotto.

| **Play 'N' Talk** | PAR | Both | 5-12 |

Players accumulate letters as they move, make words, and learn the proper phonetic sounds from a 10" LP record.

| **Dial Speller** | HAR | Both | 6-10 |

Learn to spell by association with picture and alphabet dials. Chalk, eraser, and blackboard included. Spell the word and write the word.

		INTEREST	
NAME OF TOY	MANUFACTURER	*Sex*	*Age*

Alphabet Picture Flash Cards   MBC   Both   5-7

Colored pictures of objects and alphabet letters. Games teach letter recognition and spelling.

Vowel-Links Poster Cards   MBC   Both   6-10

Cards have pictures and words with one or two missing letters. The child must insert the missing letters and pronounce the word.

**Beginning Consonant
Poster Cards**   MBC   Both   6-10

Cards have a picture and a word with one or two missing letters. The child must identify the missing letters and pronounce the word.

Phonetic Word Builder   MBC   Both   7-12

Build words, using individual cards with consonants, consonant blends, special blends, double vowels, and short and long vowel endings.

Arithmetic Quizmo   MBC   Both   7-12

Played similar to Lotto. Practice in addition, subtraction, multiplication, and division.

FIGURE-GROUND

Headstart With Music   CPT   Both   3-8

Two 12" LP records and an accompanying 28 page book help to introduce children to listening and singing skills.

Muffin In The City   YPR   Both   4-8
Muffin In The Country   YPR   Both   4-8

A record about a dog who visits a big city and the country. The many sounds of the city and the country are identified.

RETENTION AND RECALL

THE CATEGORY OF retention and recall (memory) may be further subdivided into immediate and long-term memory for meaningful and nonmeaningful material. Meaningful material is that which has significance in the child's life. An example would be daily events, stories and words. Nonmeaningful material is that which is not significant to the child. An example might be numbers, single letters of the alphabet, and phonetic pronunciation of letters. Recent research has demonstrated a high correlation between learning to read and the child's skill in immediate visual and auditory memory for nonmeaningful material. This might be expressed as the ability to associate the sounds of letters with the written symbol (letter).

VISUAL MEMORY

The parent can devise games to fit this category utilizing household objects as well as daily events. Auditory cues can be employed to assist the child to develop good visual memory.

Immediate Memory

Meaningful Material

Objects, pictures, or cards can be placed in front of the child. The parent requests the child to remember the proper order; the pictures are then turned down or the objects covered, and the child is requested to name them when the parent points to them (e.g., use a marble, a rubber ball, and a dime). Place them under a cup and ask child to tell you what is under each cup as you point to them.

NAME OF TOY	MANUFACTURER	INTEREST Sex	Age
12 O'Clock High Cards	MBC	Both	7-15

The cards are pictures of planes used in World War II. The object is to collect planes in categories.

96

| NAME OF TOY | MANUFACTURER | INTEREST | |
| | | *Sex* | *Age* |

Concentration   MBC   Both   10+

Players move numbered slides to find matching gift cards. As matches are made more of the puzzle is revealed on the board. The first to solve the puzzle wins.

Junior Memory Game   CPT   Both   4-10

Child must remember location of matching cards. Cards may also be used as cues for story-telling.

Educational Concentration   MBC   Both   7-12

Four categories: Color-matching, Word-matching, States, and History.

Memory Game   MBC   Both   10+

Players use their memory to locate and collect matching pairs of picture cards.

Probe   PAR   Both   8+

Each player conceals a secret word which others must try to guess by probing for the letters.

Facts-In-Five   AIC   Both   9+

Players are assigned five letters and five categories of subject matter. How many words or names can you come up with that start with the assigned letter and fit the classification?

Educational Password Game   MBC   Both   10+

Players must guess words from clues (antonyms, synonyms, and word association).

Nonmeaningful Material

Play Concentration with a regular deck of cards. All cards are placed face down and child turns them up one at a time and attempts to match them in number pairs.

		INTEREST	
NAME OF TOY	MANUFACTURER	Sex	Age

Go Fish   Many   Both   5-8

Played with a regular deck of cards. Each player requests a number or a suit from the other players.

Long-term Memory

Meaningful Material

The child has a multitude of visual experiences every day. Parents can have the child relate these events at the end of a day by asking specific questions about the events.

One-To-Ten Counting Books   MCI   Both   3-5

Colorful books which encourage the child to associate number symbols with appropriate number of objects.

Animal Fun   MBC   Both   3-8

Animals are fitted into appropriate jungle scenes. Letters are provided so the child can spell out the animals' names upon identification.

Learn-to-Write Letter Cards   MBC   Both   6-8

Reusable cards on which the child traces printed letters with crayons. Manuscript and cursive letters are included.

Pairs—Word Game   MBC   Both   6-9

Contains three sets of cards to match: picture-picture, picture-word, word-word.

Animals and Their Young   MBC   Both   6-10

The child matches animal pictures and their names to build his vocabulary.

NAME OF TOY	MANUFACTURER	INTEREST	
		Sex	*Age*

Play 'N' Talk   PAR   Both   5-12

Players accumulate letters as they move, make words, and learn the proper phonetic sounds from a 10" LP record.

Dial 'N' Spell   MBC   Both   4-8

A telephone dial on cards. Child spells words by dialing and when spelled correctly arrow points to the object.

Key-Kit Spelling   SHI   Both   4-7

Colorful picture cards with alphabet letters to spell the name of the object. Key-cards are notched so that only the correct letters fit. A coloring workbook is included.

Key-Kit Spelling   SHI   Both   5-8

Colorful picture cards with alphabet letters to spell the name of the object. Key-cards are notched so that only the correct letters fit. A coloring workbook is included.

Key-Kit Arithmetic   SHI   Both   4-7

Colorful picture cards are notched so that only the correct number fits, to teach basic number concepts. A coloring workbook is included.

Key-Kit Arithmetic   SHI   Both   5-8

Colorful picture cards are notched so that only the correct number fits, to teach basic number concepts. A coloring workbook is included.

Anagrams   SRC   Both   5-8

Lettered tiles are used as word and sentence builders.

Alphabet Sorting Tray Kit   MBC   Both   5-8

Individual compartments on a board for sorting letters and building simple words.

NAME OF TOY	MANUFACTURER	INTEREST Sex	Age

Alphabet Picture Flash Cards   MBC   Both   5-7
  Colored pictures of objects and alphabet letters. Games teach letter recognition and spelling.

Link Numbers   MBC   Both   6-8
  Games to learn beginning number concepts.

Bangaroo   AMS   Both   8+
  A plastic spinner propels balls into scoring pockets, which results in the acquisition of letters. They are used to spell words.

Scrabble For Juniors   SRC   Both   6-12
  A word and picture version of the Scrabble game. Players draw letters which are combined to form words. One side of the board has an easy pictorial version and the other side a more advanced version.

Vowel-Links Poster Cards   MBC   Both   6-10
  Cards have pictures and words with one or two missing letters. The child must insert the missing letters and pronounce the word.

Beginning Consonant Poster Cards MBC   Both   6-10
  Cards have a picture and a word with one or two missing letters. The child must identify the missing letters and pronounce the word.

Scrabble   SRC   Both   6+
  A crossword game. Players draw letters which must be combined to form words appropriate for the spaces on the board.

Sentence Builder   MBC   Both   6-10
  Alphabet letters and basic words, to build words and sentences.

NAME OF TOY	MANUFACTURER	INTEREST	
		Sex	*Age*

Phonetic Word Builder   MBC   Both   7-12

Build words, using individual cards with consonants, consonant blends, special blends, double vowels, and short and long vowel endings.

Spill and Spell   CCE   Both   6+

Fifteen cubes used to spell words.

Economo Sentence Builder   MBC   Both   7-12

Word recognition and sentence building games.

Arithmetic Quizmo   MBC   Both   7-12

Played similar to Lotto. Practice in addition, subtraction, multiplication, and division.

Dig   PAR   Both   8+

Players scoop out letters and form words of the subject named on the cards.

Keyword   PAR   Both   8+

This is a crossword game.

Perquackey   LAK   Both   8+

A word game played with alphabet dice.

Jotto   JOT   Both   8+

A word game involving spelling for points.

Numble   CPT   Both   9+

Game is similar to Scrabble. One builds number sequences that total a given amount and are divisible by a certain number.

The Winning Touch   EFG   Both   9+

The game is played like Scrabble but teaches multiplication.

Nonmeaningful Material

It is necessary for the parent to improvise here. One can arrange colored blocks or cards in a particular pattern, the complexity determined by the child's ability, and tell him that the game is to see how long he can remember. Objects or two-dimensional symbols can, of course, be substituted. The variables, degree of abstractness, number of stimuli, complexity of the pattern, and duration of the memory requirement, can be independently changed with increasing ability.

AUDITORY MEMORY

In this particular category there are very few available items. It is hoped that toy manufacturers will be stimulated to develop further games which will be of use in this connection. The parent can devise simple games using household objects which would assist the child in developing skills in this area. Visual cues can be employed frequently to assist the child develop good auditory memory.

Immediate Memory

Meaningful Material

"I went on a trip and took a cow with me." (Animal names, names of objects, et cetera). This sentence is repeated, and a different animal or object is added to the list each time. The child must attempt to repeat the animals or objects in the correct order.

The parent can read simple stories to the child and ask specific questions about the material read.

The parent can ask the child to bring objects in the room to him in sequence, e.g. "Bring me the ash tray, book, and envelope." The number of objects can be increased.

A variation would be "Put the pencil in the box and put the box on the chair." The child must attempt to follow the verbal sequence of commands. A normal child can respond to four such commissions.

NAME OF TOY	MANUFACTURER	INTEREST	
		Sex	*Age*

Educational Password Game　　MBC　　　　Both　　　10+

Players must guess words from clues (antonyms, synonyms, and word association).

Nonmeaningful Material

The parent can request that the child remember addresses, birthdates, ages, or telephone numbers of friends and relatives which are read to him. Simple rewards should be provided for accomplishment.

Go Fish　　　　　　　　Many　　　　Both　　　5-8

Play with a regular deck of cards. Each player requests a number or a suit from the other players.

Long-term Memory

Meaningful Material

The parent can ask child question about stories read on the day before.

The parents can have the child memorize simple nursery rhymes, poems, and songs. This can progress to very lengthy recitations.

Alphabet Sorting Tray Kit　　MBC　　　　Both　　　5-8

Individual compartments on a board for sorting letters and building simple words.

Alphabet Picture Flash Cards　　MBC　　　Both　　　5-7

Colored pictures of objects and alphabet letters. Games teach letter recognition and spelling.

Link Numbers　　　　　　MBC　　　　Both　　　6-8

Games to learn beginning number concepts.

NAME OF TOY	MANUFACTURER	INTEREST Sex	Age

Vowel-Links Poster Cards   MBC   Both   6-10
   Cards have pictures and words with one or two missing letters.
   The child must insert the missing letters and pronounce the
   word.

Beginning Consonant Poster Cards   MBC   Both   6-10
   Cards have a picture and a word with one or two missing
   letters. The child must identify the missing letters and pronounce the word.

Sentence Builder   MBC   Both   6-10
   Alphabet letters and basic words, to build words and sentences.

Phonetic Word Builder   MBC   Both   7-12
   Build words, using individual cards with consonants, consonant
   blends, special blends, double vowels, and short and long
   vowel endings.

Economo Sentence Builder   MBC   Both   7-12
   Word recognition and sentence building games.

Arithmetic Quizmo   MBC   Both   7-12
   Played similar to Lotto. Practice in addition, subtraction,
   multiplication, and division.

Nonmeaningful Material

   The parent can request that the child remember various
telephone numbers associated with friends and relatives. Including this in both short-term and long-term memory implies varying the length of time between retention and recall.

Play 'N' Talk   PAR   Both   5-12
   Players accumulate letters as they move, make words, and learn
   the proper phonetic sounds from a 10" LP record.

CONCEPTUALIZATION

CONCEPTUALIZATION IS SEEN as a large category, including all higher mental functions. This involves skills in understanding novel relationships, abstract reasoning, problem-solving, and other tasks. Included in this category are most of the functions that determine intelligence in older children and adults in an intellectual society. There is every reason to believe that this function is influenced by environment. Evidence which bears on this question would include such things as the data which shows that the intelligence quotient of adopted children matches that of the adoptive parents more closely than that of the natural parents.

Many toys have a broad range of applicability for conceptual skills depending upon how they are used. Blocks may be piled meaninglessly or may represent a wide variety of objects and teach structured relations, various mathematical concepts, and aesthetic values. The way the child utilizes games and toys will relate closely to the parents' interest and participation. If, when the child wants to show them a block construction, they reply "That's nice. Go build something else," they will have different results than if the parents praise the child, get down on the floor, and ask questions about the structure, such as "What is that part? How clever to use that block for support. That's an interesting way to use color. Wouldn't it be fun to live in this kind of house? Would you like to save this to show Daddy? I know he'll be very proud." It must be emphasized that there is no substitute for personal parental stimulation, and that the parent who feels this is entirely up to the school is in error. This is particularly true of a child who experiences difficulties in learning.

NAME OF TOY	MANUFACTURER	INTEREST Sex	Age
Stacking Ring Set	**HCM**	**Both**	1½-3

Four different sized rings fit on a wooden peg.

NAME OF TOY	MANUFACTURER	INTEREST	
		Sex	*Age*

Nesting Toys PMC Both 1-3
1. Nesting Bowls
2. Billy and His Barrels
3. Building Cups
4. Stacking Pyramid
5. Nesting Nuts and Bolts

Stacking Toys MCI Both 2-4

An elephant, an owl, and a Mexican man made of several wooden pieces which are stacked in a precise order.

Lacing Shoe FPT Both 2-4

Plastic shoe with laces for lacing. Geometric shaped figures must be matched to the correct slots in order to fill in the shoe.

Giant Rack-A-Stack FPT Both 1-3

Ten rings fit on a cane in size sequence.

Form Boxes PMC Both 1½-5
1. Postal Station
2. Lock-up Barn

Child fits twelve varicolored blocks of four shapes into respective slots in the tops of the boxes.

**Goldilocks and The Three
Bears Playhouse** FPT Both 2-5

The geometrically shaped figures must be matched to the slots in the top of the playhouse.

Blocks PMC Both 1½-8

Colored and plain wooden blocks of varied shapes and sizes for building.

NAME OF TOY	MANUFACTURER	INTEREST	
		Sex	*Age*

Bags of Blocks　　　　　　　HAL　　　　Both　　　2-5
Colored and natural finish ⅞" scale wood blocks in ten different shapes.

Educational Blocks　　　　　FPT　　　　Both　　　2-5
Varied-shaped wooden blocks for building.

Hi-Lo Interlocking Blocks　　HAL　　　　Both　　　1½-4
Indented alphabet letters on 1½" blocks that interlock for ease in building.

The Chicken in the Eggs　　PMC　　　　Both　　　3-6
Six plastic eggs, graduated in size, are taken apart to find the chick.

All By Himself—Book　　　CPT　　　　Both　　　3-5
Cloth book with washable objects, to teach child to dress himself—button, snap, tie, and zip.

Sandbox Play　　　　　　Many　　　　Both　　　2-5
Give the child different-sized bottles, cans, jars, funnels, pans, sieves for filling and dumping the sand.

Busy Board　　　　　　　BSC　　　　Both　　　2-5
Wooden board with bolts, nuts, hinges, et cetera with which children can experiment.

Art-Tube Finger Paints　　PAR　　　　Both　　　3-10
Child creates his own picture with the use of finger paints.

NAME OF TOY	MANUFACTURER	INTEREST Sex	Age

Painting   Many   Both   3+
   1. Water colors with brush
   2. Dri-mark water colors
   3. Tempera

Sculpey   PLY   Both   3+
Polyform   PLY   Both   3+
Plastic modeling material does not harden in the air but hardens when baked in home oven. Objects can be carved and painted.

Clay   MBC   Both   3+
   1. Clayrite
   2. Tru-Model
Artificial clay used to create objects. May be reused again and again.

Clay Modeling   CPT   Both   3+
   1. Playdough or artificial clay
   2. Modo clay—hardens without firing
   3. Cera clay—oven fire at home
   4. Pottery clay—must be fired at high temperatures
Objects can be painted or glazed.

Dolls   Many   Girls   3-12
Dress and undress dolls and encourage imaginary play.

Action Soldier—G. I. Joe   HCM   Both   5-8
Ten-inch male doll has numerous outfits for dressing, and play equipment lends to action play.

Paper Dolls   MBC   Girls   5-12
For the young child, start with large dolls and uncomplicated clothes to be cut out.

NAME OF TOY	MANUFACTURER	INTEREST	
		Sex	*Age*

Musical Instruments   Many   Both   3+

    1. Drums   5. Recorder
    2. Whistle   6. Tonette
    3. Bells   7. Maracas
    4. Xylophone   8. Guitar

Playskool-Match Ups   PMC   Both   3-6

    1. Picture Alphabet   4. Words to Spell
    2. Colors and Things   5. Animal Homes
    3. Count From 1-24   6. People and Their Jobs
    Two-Piece match-up cards.

Liddle Kiddle Games   MTI   Both   4-7

    1. Baby Animals
    2. Let's Go Fishing
    3. Color Bingo
In each game the child must match the top and bottom halves of pictures.

Miniature Series   MCI   Both   1½-4

Vivid picture stories of familiar subject matter such as shopping, the farm, the zoo in 3-D.

One-To-Ten Counting Books   MCI   Both   3-5

Colorful books which encourage the child to associate number symbols with appropriate number of objects.

Make-It-Box   MBC   Both   4-10

Variety of activities (e.g. make 3-D objects, mobiles). Stencils, crayons and paints are supplied.

Coordination Board   SIF   Both   2-4

Four geometric shapes in different colors in a puzzle form. The child must match a cutout to the appropriate space.

NAME OF TOY	MANUFACTURER	INTEREST	
		Sex	*Age*

Shapes, Colors and Forms   CCE   Both   2-4
Rubber forms of graduated sizes fit into a wooden tray.

Difference Puzzles   SIM   Both   3-6
Puzzles teach difference of shapes and sizes of objects.

Peg Leveling Board   BSC   Both   2-5
Nine wooden pegs, graduated in size, fit into holes in a board.

Peg Grading Board   BSC   Both   2-5
Child must sort and grade thirty wooden pegs for size and color to fit into a board with thirty holes.

Peg and Shape Sort Board   BSC   Both   2-5
Four geometric wooden shapes with holes in them to fit on pegs attached to a board.

Tinker Box   CHI   Both   2-4
Plastic tool box into which large screws, nuts, and bolts can be put with the aid of a plastic hammer, screwdriver, and wrench.

Counting Frame   PMC   Both   3-8
Wooden beads slide on rods on a large frame. Helps child learn basic colors and simple arithmetic.

Match Mates   CPT   Both   3-6
Ten jigsaw puzzles, cut in half, have numbers on the top half to correspond with the number of objects on the bottom. Tops and bottoms fit only when correctly matched.

NAME OF TOY	MANUFACTURER	INTEREST	
		Sex	*Age*

Fit-A-Square CCE Both 2-4

Teaches child colors and form associations by providing him with sixteen cutout rubber discs into which forty-eight pieces in twelve different shapes fit.

Judgments and Readiness CPT Both 4-8

Colored rubber squares, circles, and triangles are composed of five or more concentric outlines which can be taken apart and fit together to make a solid figure.

Magnetic Construction Set BSC Both 2-6

Horseshoe magnet, a number of disc and bar magnets, and various-shaped metal pieces for constructing objects.

New Tot Railroad PMC Both 2-9

Twenty-eight piece plastic railroad set for beginners. Child builds in many ways.

Skaneateles Transportation Sets PMC Both 2-10

Wooden railroad sets—tracks, cars, et cetera.

Construction Kit MCI Both 3-5

Nuts, bolts, and connectors (wooden) are joined to form objects and toys.

Workbench PMC Both 2-5

A wooden bench with wooden nuts, bolts, screws, and nails which can be manipulated.

Wood Toy Builder PMC Both 3-8

Construction kit consists of wooden girders, nuts, bolts, screws, and appropriate plastic tools.

NAME OF TOY	MANUFACTURER	INTEREST	
		Sex	*Age*

Lots-A-Links AMS Both 3-5

Plastic multicolored snap-close links which can make chains, bracelets, et cetera.

Wood Playmates CPT Both 4-6

Seven wood bodies, four heads, and a quantity of arms and legs go together to make people.

Landscape Peg Set PMC Both 2½-6

Child constructs landscapes with pegs and wooden shapes.

Play Chest HCM Both 3-5

Wooden chest complete with blackboard, pegboard, mallet, and pegs.

Peg Desk PMC Both 3-8

Desk with attached seat. Top of desk is a blackboard. Chalk and eraser are supplied. Under the top is a pegboard. Pegs are supplied.

Standard Hammer-Nail Set PMC Both 3-6

Twelve-inch-square composition pounding board, laying sticks, nails, and hammer. Design sheet provided.

Hammer and Nail Sets HAL Both 4-7

Pounding board 12" by 10". Colored heads of Huck, Yogi, et cetera in chipboard. Laying sticks, nails, and hammer are used to create humorous scenes.

Hammer-Nail Design Board Set CPT Both 5-10

Two hundred varied die-cut steel shapes. Hammer and nails are used to construct designs on wallboards.

| NAME OF TOY | MANUFACTURER | INTEREST | |
| | | *Sex* | *Age* |

Rubber Beaded Pegboard   **CPT**   Both   4-8
Duplicate or make designs with pegs on the board.

Bolts and Nuts Builder   **KOH**   Both   4-6
Large wooden and plastic bolts, nuts, wheels, and other parts
can be combined to form movable toys.

Giant Snap-Lock Ring and Beads   **FPT**   Both   2-4
Colored plastic parts snap together to make chains, et cetera.

Snap 'N' Play   **SIF**   Both   4-7
Wooden pieces of various shapes and sizes snap together to
make objects.

Loony Links   **AMS**   Both   5-8
Snap parts of bodies together to form animals and people.

Wooden Plane   **MCI**   Both   3-8
Forty-three wooden pieces including nuts, bolts, and connectors
which can be used for construction of many objects.

Bolt-It   **CPT**   Both   4-8
Large wooden, plastic, and metal parts to make rolling and
stationary toys from suggested designs.

Hardwood Construction Set   **MCI I**   Both   3-7
Fifty building parts nuts, bolts, screws, drilled strips, pulleys,
and four rubber tires. Wooden wrench, screwdriver, and
guide booklet provided.

Hammer and Nail Set   **CCE**   Both   4-6
Set includes a board, hammer, object blocks, nails, and sticks
to be used in creating pictures on a wallboard.

NAME OF TOY	MANUFACTURER	INTEREST	
		Sex	*Age*

Comic Corner CCE Both 3-5

Thirty-four interchangeable pegged parts to make your own street scenes. People, traffic light, and store parts are included.

Rig-A-Jig CCE Both 5-7

Colorful plastic pieces interlock to form people, animals, trucks, and geometric forms.

Take-Apart Truck and Kiddie Car PMC Both 4-6

Two over-sized vehicles which children take apart, put together, and ride. Has wooden nuts, bolts, a wrench, and a screwdriver.

Lotto EUC Both 4-8

1. **ABC Lotto**   5. **What's Missing Lotto**
2. **Zoo Lotto**   6. **Go-Together Lotto**
3. **Farm Lotto**   7. **Object Lotto**
4. **The World About Us Lotto**

The child must match the picture cards to pictures on the playing boards.

Pardon Me PAR Both 5-8

A card game. Play calls for simple counting and matching of pictures of animals.

Spell By Pictures WAC Both 4-6

Three movable bands of pictures are manipulated until three identical pictures are lined up and the correct spelling is found at the bottom.

Children's Hour CCE Both 5-10

Three games in one. Combines picture and alphabet identification with beginning number and reading skills.

| NAME OF TOY | MANUFACTURER | INTEREST | |
		Sex	*Age*
See-Ques	CPT	Both	4-7

1. **Junior**—Nursery rhymes. Nature stories.
2. **Advanced**—Many stories.
Child arranges picture cards in sequence and recreates story verbally.

Picture Sequence Cards	MBC	Both	5-8

Child must place picture cards in the correct order to tell the story. Twenty different stories are included.

What's Missing? Story Cards	MBC	Both	5-8

The child must select the missing part, to complete the picture. The pictures are labeled.

Rainbow Towers	SGH	Both	4-7

Game involving skills prerequisite for learning to count using colored bead towers.

Notchies	CPT	Both	3-5

Large plastic blocks interlock in various positions to assist the child in building precarious forms.

Interslot	MCl	Both	4-8

Thirty-four wooden pieces in six different shapes can be fit together to create structures.

Balance Building Set	MCI	Both	5-10

Fifteen odd-shaped blocks for building towers.

Blockhead	CCE	Both	6+

Many different-shaped wooden blocks are placed one on top of another. The object is to add shapes without tumbling the structure.

| NAME OF TOY | MANUFACTURER | INTEREST | |
		Sex	*Age*
Miniature Set-up Kits	MCI	Both	4-6

Wooden cutouts can be put together to form multiple familiar scenes such as school rooms, farm, airport.

Electric Train Sets	Many	Boys	5+

This category covers a variety of electric trains.

Kinder Suburbia	SIF	Both	4-8

Block city in which child decides the number of stories, types of buildings, pitch of the roof, and location on imaginary streets.

Museum Collage and			
Construction Sets	CPT	Both	4+

A collection of various materials (e.g. faille, cork, sponge, yarn, beads) for creating a collage.

Silk-Screen Set	CPT	Girls	10+

All necessary equipment and instructions are included for creating greeting cards, stationery, placemats.

Creating With Wood	Many	Boys	5+

Use tools and a pattern to make simple objects (e.g. go-carts, simple furniture).

Fun Time Clock	WAC	Both	4-7

Hands, gears, and other parts can be taken apart and put back together.

Junior Workshop	HAR	Both	3-5

Four plastic tools and nails to use with plastic lumber.

Mr. Builder's Home Workshop	HAR	Both	3-5

Ten plastic tools, nails, and lumber for construction.

NAME OF TOY	MANUFACTURER	INTEREST	
		Sex	*Age*

Across The Continent — PAR — Both — 6+

Players tour the United States following prearranged itineraries. Moves are controlled by dice. The map shows principal cities, crops, industries, et cetera.

Lincoln Logs — PMC — Both — 4-8
— HAL — Both — 4-8

Three-quarter-inch hardwood logs and other material for construction of buildings.

Tinker Toys — Many — Both — 3-8

Assorted wooden Tinker Toy pieces and moving parts used for construction.

Lego System Blocks — CCE — Both — 4-8

Interlocking blocks of different shapes and primary colors can be combined to form sturdy structures.

Block City — CCE — Both — 5-8

These sets supply plastic interlocking blocks cut for building houses, stores, and buildings.

American Plastic Bricks — HAL — Both — 5-8

Interlocking plastic bricks can be used to create many different objects.

Building Models — Many — Boys — 6-14

Precut plastic or wooden parts must be glued together following a pattern to make objects such as cars, boats, planes.

Ship in Bottle — CPT — Boys — 8-12

Child must glue precut parts of a boat and place in bottle, which is then glued together.

NAME OF TOY	MANUFACTURER	INTEREST Sex	Age

Glass Blowing Set   CPT   Both   16+

All equipment included for blowing your own creations.

**Preschool and Kindergarten
Science Kit**   CPT   Both   4-6

The kit includes compass, magnets, magnifying glasses, thermometer, et cetera for assisting the child to learn about science.

Military Construction Sets   HCM   Boys   5-8

Interlocking plastic parts build bridges, observation towers, et cetera.

Asymmetric Space Construction   CPT   Both   4-8

Sixty pieces of various-sized rods and dowels for construction of various objects.

Snap-Eze Playforms   CCE   Both   5-7

A collection of unbreakable plastic rods, wheels, and blocks all interlocking to build a wide range of objects (e.g. people, houses, cars).

Inventatoy   CPT   Both   4-8

Dowels and connector parts can be manipulated to form toys with movable parts.

Constructioneer   HAL   Both   5-8

Interlocking plastic blocks in a multitude of different shapes are used to build complicated objects.

Magnasticks   CCE   Both   5-7

Magnetic plates hold metal construction parts together while building structures.

| NAME OF TOY | MANUFACTURER | INTEREST | |
		Sex	*Age*

Woodcraft Parts, Senior Set CPT Boys 6-12
An assortment of wooden handles, spools, wheels, and balls which can be combined in various ways with the aid of nails.

Sewing Machine Set HCM Girls 5-8
Sets include miniature machine that operates by hand; needles, thread, thimble, scissors, patterns, and material are included.

Flexagons CCE Both 5-8
Four cardboard squares and triangles assemble with rubber-bands to form 3-D boats, houses, and geometric forms.

Geodestix Construction Kit CPT Both 6-12
Sturdy rods and plastic connector joints can be manipulated to form interesting 3-D designs.

Bend 'N' Build Construction Set CCE Both 6-10
Big unbreakable plastic tubes for construction of large-scale models. Connectors link tubes, and parts are movable.

Constructo Straws PAR Both 6-10
Two hundred flexible plastic straws can be joined to make large-scale models.

Home Team Baseball SRC Boys 6+
An indoor version of America's favorite game.

Batta Hai CAD Both 6+
This game combines the simplicity of Lotto with the elements of strategy. Each player has a board and matches cards called by another player. Cards have faces, numbers, and domino matching.

| NAME OF TOY | MANUFACTURER | INTEREST | |
		Sex	*Age*

Slate Bingo WAC Both 4-8

A bingo game where children learn their ABC's. Spinner dial shows twenty-four objects that are matched on cards along with letters.

Giant Tic-Tac-Toe HCM Both 6-10

A large version of the classic game.

Sorting Box Combination MCI Both 4-8

This toy is designed to teach colors and numbers. Wooden strips of different colors and with objects painted on them are matched to master strips.

Play 'N' Talk PAR Both 5-12

Players accumulate letters as they move, make words, and learn the proper phonetic sounds from a 10" LP record.

Spellit CAD Both 4-8

A dial in the center spells, adds, and subtracts. If players make the correct move, the correct picture appears in the center of the dial.

Kalah KAL Both 6+

Helps children of any age acquire mathematical concepts.

On-Sets CPT Both 6+

A game to teach new math concepts.

Smarty EFG Both 7-12

Arithmetic-Bingo game which teaches addition, subtraction, and multiplication.

NAME OF TOY	MANUFACTURER	INTEREST	
		Sex	*Age*

Spell Master   SGH   Both   4-7

One hundred pictures with names to spell and eighty plastic letters so constructed that only the correct letters fit.

Alphabet Sorting Tray Kit   MBC   Both   5-8

Individual compartments on a board for sorting letters and building simple words.

Dial 'N' Spell   MBC   Both   4-8

A telephone dial on cards. Child spells words by dialing and when spelled right, arrow points to correct object.

Key-Kit Spelling   SHI   Both   4-7

Colorful picture cards with alphabet letters to spell the name of the object. Keycards are notched so that only the correct letters fit. A coloring workbook is included.

Key-Kit Spelling   SHI   Both   5-8

Colorful picture cards with alphabet letters to spell the name of the object. Keycards are notched so that only the correct letters fit. A coloring workbook is included.

Key-Kit Arithmetic   SHI   Both   4-7

Colorful picture cards are notched, so that only the correct number fits, to teach basic number concepts. A coloring workbook is included.

Key-Kit Arithmetic   SHI   Both   5-8

Colorful picture cards are notched, so that only the correct number fits, to teach basic number concepts. A coloring workbook is included.

NAME OF TOY	MANUFACTURER	INTEREST	
		Sex	*Age*

Alphabet Picture Flash Cards   MBC   Both   5-7

Colored pictures of objects and alphabet letters. Games teach letter recognition and spelling.

Animals and Their Young   MBC   Both   6-10

The child matches animal pictures and their names to build his vocabulary.

Link Numbers   MBC   Both   6-8

Games to learn beginning number concepts.

Wide World   PAR   Both   8+

A board game where players fly to various countries and win points by bringing products home from each area.

12 O'Clock High Cards   MBC   Both   7-15

The cards are pictures of planes used in World War II. The object is to collect planes in categories.

Authors   PAR   Both   8+

A card game. The object is to collect as many complete sets of authors and their works.

Lithography Kit   CPT   Both   12+

Materials are provided for children to learn how to print cards, pictures, et cetera.

Milles Bornes   PAR   Both   6+

A card game. Players travel cross country earning mileage points while overcoming travel hazards.

NAME OF TOY	MANUFACTURER	INTEREST	
		Sex	*Age*

The Chase   CAD   Both   6-12

This is an exciting rabbit-hound chase through the wilds of the Florida Everglades. A forty-page booklet explains what locations are considered dangerous.

Sorry   PAR   Both   8+

A board game involving a chase to the finish line. Moves are governed by cards drawn from a deck.

Parker Baseball   PAR   Boys   7+

A board game similar to real baseball. The pitcher and batter choose their plays.

Clue   PAR   Both   7+

A board game. Players attempt to solve the mystery that has taken place in an old mansion. Players get clues from cards.

Beginning Consonant Poster Cards   MBC   Both   6-10

Cards have a picture and a word with one or two missing letters. The child must identify the missing letters and pronounce the word.

Vowel-Links Poster Cards   MBC   Both   6-10

Cards have pictures and words with one or two missing letters. The child must insert the missing letters and pronounce the word.

Sentence Builder   MBC   Both   6-10

Alphabet letters and basic words, to build words and sentences.

Phonetic Word Builder   MBC   Both   7-12

Build words, using individual cards with consonants, consonant blends, special blends, double vowels, and short and long vowel endings.

NAME OF TOY	MANUFACTURER	INTEREST	
		Sex	*Age*

Economo Sentence Builder   MBC   Both   7-12
   Word-recognition and sentence-building games.

Arithmetic Quizmo   MBC   Both   7-12
   Played similar to Lotto. Practice in addition, subtraction, multiplication, and division.

Automobile Racing Game   PAR   Boys   8+
   This is a board game of car racing involving authentic tactics
   to complete the course.

Touring   PAR   Both   7+
   A card game. Players must overcome mishaps of an auto tour
   to reach the goal.

Dogfight   MBC   Both   10+
   A command-decision game based on World War I. Players
   decide the strategy of combat among armies.

Seven Seas   CAD   Both   8+
   A travel game where players buy and sell cargo on the seven
   seas. The object is to make money while crossing the seas
   rapidly.

Yacht Race   PAR   Both   8+
   A board game where players race boats, using authentic
   strategies while the wind shifts direction constantly.

Broadside   MBC   Both   10+
   Players fight sea battles, using authentic tactics.

NAME OF TOY	MANUFACTURER	INTEREST	
		Sex	*Age*

As The World Turns PAR Both 10+

Players move their men to various cities on a board as they attempt to travel around the world. Penalties force players to uncivilized areas and they must find their way out.

Careers PAR Both 10+

This board game involves the challenge of attaining fame and fortune. The player must decide how to attain his fortune and may have many setbacks.

Politics PAR Both 10+

A board game where players campaign across the country trying for enough electoral votes to become President.

Conflict PAR Both 10+

A board war game where players plan military strategy in an attempt to win a war.

Risk PAR Both 8+

This is a board game involving armies struggling for power and conquest of territory.

Pit PAR Both 8+

A card game. Players bill, sell, and attempt to "corner the market" in wheat, oats, and other grains.

Finance PAR Both 8+

Players buy, sell, and trade property in an attempt to gain possession of all the property.

Tycoon PAR Both 8+

A board game where players purchase, trade, and sell shares in six large corporations in an attempt to accumulate wealth.

NAME OF TOY	MANUFACTURER	INTEREST	
		Sex	Age

Rich Uncle   PAR   **Both**   8+

A board game where players start out with $10,000 and attempt to increase the sum to $50,000 by investing.

Monopoly   **PAR**   **Both**   8+

This game deals with buying and selling real estate, using paper money. Players attempt to bankrupt each other.

Take 12   PAR   **Both**   8+

Players throw dice and attempt to match their count with combinations of twelve white cubes.

Paper Plays   **CPT**   **Both**   8-12

Patterned paper is folded and cut to form 3-D sculptures.

Erector Set   GIL   **Boys**   8+

A variety of metal building components and an electric motor, for building structures.

Junior Clockmaker Kit   RBI   **Boys**   10+

Put a real cuckoo clock together and make it run.

Dominoes   HAL   **Both**   6+
                     MBC   **Both**   6+

The regular domino game which requires matching and number skills.

Concentration   MBC   **Both**   10+

Players move numbered slides to find matching gift cards. As matches are made, more of the puzzle is revealed on the board. The first to solve the puzzle wins.

| NAME OF TOY | MANUFACTURER | INTEREST | |
		Sex	*Age*

Rock-O-Card Game   MBC   Both   10+

By drawing and discarding, players try to get cards in a numerical sequence from low to high.

Electrical Invention Box   CPT   Boys   6-12

Kit includes wire, bulbs, sockets, switches, buzzers, motors, et cetera. No instructions are included, to encourage the child to experiment.

Electrical Invention Box   CPT   Boys   6-10

Contains 26 pieces (light bulb, sockets, switches, bell, buzzer, et cetera) which are operated by a harmless six-volt battery.

Junior Electro-Experimental Set   RBI   Boys   10-16

Child learns the principle of electricity by putting together simple, safe, everyday components.

Sewing   Many   Girls   10+

Sewing by hand or with the aid of a machine, using regular patterns and various types of materials.

Mandalay   FOR   Both   10+

The object is to rebuild the tower of discs on another needle, never playing a larger disc on a smaller disc and moving only one disc at a time.

WfF'N Poof   CPT   Both   8+

Twenty-one progressively more difficult games. The games use symbols for words. Players are rewarded for logical thinking.

NAME OF TOY	MANUFACTURER	INTEREST	
		Sex	*Age*

Pegity   PAR   Both   8+

The object is to get five pegs of one color in an uninterrupted row while blocking opponents.

Tangle   SRC   Both   8+

Players use geometric shapes which are moved across a board to form a pattern and block the opponent's pattern.

Selbright Chess For Juniors   SRC   Both   6-12

The game of chess is simplified for junior. Players move men across the board in an attempt to capture opponent's men and reach the opposite side of the board.

Camelot   PAR   Both   8+

A board game where players move knights and men-at-arms to capture the opponent's castle.

Checkers   SRC   Both   7+
                         MBC   Both   7+
                         FAR   Both   7+
                         HAL   Both   7+

Two players must calculate how they can move checkers on a board in order to capture the opponent's checkers.

Troke   SRC   Both   8+

A strategy game combining the skills of checkers and chess. Interlocking towers, walls and moats are maneuvered across a board to be assembled on the goal line.

Stratego   MBC   Both   10+

Similar to chess but the object is to move men in an effort to capture the opponent's flag.

| NAME OF TOY | MANUFACTURER | INTEREST | |
		Sex	Age
Chess	**MBC**	**Both**	**7+**
	HAL	**Both**	**7+**

Two players must calculate how they can move their chessmen across the board in order to trap the opponent's king.

| **Anagrams** | **SRC** | **Both** | **5-8** |

Lettered tiles are used as word and sentence builders.

| **Spill and Spell** | **CCE** | **Both** | **6+** |

Fifteen cubes used to spell words.

| **Scrabble for Juniors** | **SRC** | **Both** | **6-12** |

A word and picture version of the Scrabble game. Players draw letters which are combined to form words. One side of the board has an easy pictorial version and the other side a more advanced version.

| **Bangaroo** | **AMS** | **Both** | **8+** |

A plastic spinner propels balls into scoring pockets, resulting in the acquisition of letters. They are used to spell words.

| **Dig** | **PAR** | **Both** | **8+** |

Players scoop out letters and form words of the subject named on the cards.

| **Jeopardy** | **MBC** | **Both** | **10+** |

Players start with the answer and must construct a correct question to win.

| **Facts-In-Five** | **AIC** | **Both** | **9+** |

Players are assigned five letters and five categories of subject matter. How many words or names can you come up with that start with the assigned letter and fit the classification?

NAME OF TOY	MANUFACTURER	INTEREST Sex	Age

The Winning Touch EFG Both 9+
   The game is played like Scrabble but teaches multiplication.

Jotto JOT Both 8+
   A word game involving spelling for points.

Scrabble SRC Both 6+
   A crossword game. Players draw letters which must be combined to form words appropriate for the spaces on the board.

Perquackey LAK Both 8+
   A word game played with alphabet dice.

Probe PAR Both 8+
   Each player conceals a secret word which others must try to guess by probing for the letters.

Numble CPT Both 9+
   Game is similar to Scrabble. One builds number sequences that total a given amount and are divisible by a certain number.

Keyword PAR Both 8+
   This is a crossword game.

Educational Password Game MBC Both 10+
   Players must guess words from clues (antonyms, synonyms, and word association).

EXPRESSION

FINE MOTOR

Fine-motor tasks may be viewed from two vantage points as precursors to school activity. This is true first in the sense that dexterous use of the hands and fingers is a requirement for satisfactory handwriting. The other, and somewhat indirect advantage that occurs when performing fine-motor tasks is improvement in ability to remain in one location and focus on a task. The nature of fine-motor tasks is such that the tasks are usually performed while the person is sitting down or standing in one place. Skill required to perform tasks is based on size of materials, structural complexity, and dimension and timing of reflexes.

In the case of young children, it is often necessary for the parent to demonstrate the use of the toy or game once or twice before the child is able to participate in constructive play. The child will enjoy playing many of these games alone as well as with the parent.

| | | INTEREST | |
NAME OF TOY	MANUFACTURER	Sex	Age
Alphabet Blocks	HAL	Both	2-5

One-and-one-half-inch blocks with raised, colored alphabet letters for building and to familiarize child with alphabet.

Cubical Counting Blocks	MBC	Both	3-6

Use colored blocks to develop number concepts and learn colors while building objects.

Blocks	PMC	Both	1½-8

Colored and plain wooden blocks of varied shapes and sizes for building.

NAME OF TOY	MANUFACTURER	INTEREST	
		Sex	*Age*

Bags of Blocks HAL Both 2-5
Colored and natural finish ⅞" scale wood blocks in ten different shapes.

Educational Blocks FPT Both 2-5
Varied-shaped wooden blocks for building.

Puzzle Cubes MCI Both 4-7
Twelve cubes can be made into six different color pictures. Guides are included in box.

Changeable Blocks HAL Both 4-7
Over four-million faces can be created by piecing the blocks in different manners.

Design Blocks CCE Both 4-7
Square colored wooden blocks. Child combines solid colors and diagonals to form endless designs.

Parquetry Blocks PMC Both 3-6
Various-shaped wooden blocks fit together to make colorful designs. Design suggestions included.

Art-Tube Finger Paints PAR Both 3-10
Child creates his own picture with the use of finger paints. **Note:** Finger paints allow for the production of a pleasant and permanent result, even with marked limitations in fine-motor skill.

Picture Dominoes HAR Both 4-7
Twenty-eight giant dominoes with pictures on one side and dots on the other. **Note:** In games such as dominoes the required motor skills are peripheral to the central point of the game and permit the child to develop skills without conscious awareness.

NAME OF TOY	MANUFACTURER	INTEREST	
		Sex	*Age*

Jolly Time Dominoes   MBC   Both   4-7

Colored pictures on one side and regular dominoes on the reverse side. The object is to match.

Jumbo Color Dominoes   PMC   Both   3-6
    MBC   Both   5-10

Color dot dominoes for visual matching to teach counting and colors.

Animal Dominoes   FAR   Both   4-7

The object is to match the animals to those that have been played.

Nesting Toys   PMC   Both   1-3
    1. **Nesting Bowls**
    2. **Billy and His Barrels**
    3. **Building Cups**
    4. **Stacking Pyramid**
    5. **Nesting Nuts and Bolts**

Nesting Blocks   MCI   Both   3-5

Wooden stacking blocks with pictures painted on the sides.

Clay   MBC   Both   3+
    1. **Clayrite**
    2. **Tru-Model**

Artificial clay used to create objects. May be reused again and again.

Clay Modeling   CPT   Both   3+
    1. **Playdough or artificial clay**
    2. **Modo clay**—hardens without firing
    3. **Cera clay**—oven fire at home
    4. **Pottery clay**—must be fired at high temperatures

Objects can be painted or glazed. **Note:** Modeling materials have a wide range of applicability.

NAME OF TOY	MANUFACTURER	INTEREST	
		Sex	*Age*
Sculpey	**PLY**	**Both**	**3+**
Polyform	**PLY**	**Both**	**3+**

Plastic modeling material does not harden in the air, but hardens when baked in home oven. Objects can be carved and painted.

Hi-Lo Interlocking Blocks	**HAL**	**Both**	**1½-4**

Indented alphabet letters on 1½" blocks that interlock for ease in building.

Beginner Inlay Puzzles	**SIF**	**Both**	**1½-5**

Each picture is one separate unit that fits only one space. There are five to six pictures per wooden frame.

Clothespin Dairy Wagon	**PMC**	**Both**	**1½-3**

Push-pull toy has two small plastic milk bottles on wooden milk truck. Six colorful clothespins to drop into bottles. Truck makes a motor sound when pulled.

Fill 'N' Dump Bottle	**CCE**	**Both**	**2-4**

Quart plastic bottles with spools and clothespins.

Giant Rack-A-Stack	**FPT**	**Both**	**1-3**

Ten rings fit on a cane in size sequence.

Form Boxes	**PMC**	**Both**	**1½-5**

  1. Postal Station
  2. Lock-up Barn
Child fits twelve varicolored blocks of four shapes into respective slots in the tops of the boxes.

Goldilocks and The Three			
Bears Playhouse	**FPT**	**Both**	**2-5**

The geometrically shaped figures must be matched to the slots in the top of the playhouse.

NAME OF TOY	MANUFACTURER	INTEREST Sex	Age

Coordination Board　　　SIF　　　Both　　　2-4

Four geometric shapes in different colors in a puzzle form. The child must match a cutout to the appropriate space.

Playboards　　　SIM　　　Both　　　2-5

Simple, one-piece wooden puzzles with knobs. Pictures of familiar objects.

Round Puzzles　　　MCI　　　Both　　　1½-4

Wooden one-piece and multipiece puzzles with and without knobs.

Shapes, Colors, and Forms　　　CCE　　　Both　　　2-4

Rubber forms of graduated sizes fit into a wooden tray.

Boo Boo Blocks　　　LAK　　　Both　　　2-5

Match heads and bodies of animals painted on interlocking two piece blocks.

Poly Blocks and Rods　　　PMC　　　Both　　　2-5

Large plastic blocks in three shapes to fit over ⅝" dowels.

Stacking Ring Set　　　HCM　　　Both　　　1½-3

Four different-sized rings fit on a wooden peg.

Stacking Toys　　　MCI　　　Both　　　2-4

An elephant, an owl, and a Mexican man made of several wooden pieces which are stacked in a precise order.

Peg and Shape Sort Board　　　BSC　　　Both　　　2-5

Four geometric wooden shapes with holes in them to fit on pegs attached to a board.

NAME OF TOY	MANUFACTURER	INTEREST	
		Sex	*Age*

Difference Puzzles   SIM   Both   3-6

Puzzles teach difference of shapes and sizes of objects.

Peg Leveling Board   BSC   Both   2-5

Nine wooden pegs, graduated in size, fit into holes in a board.

Lacing Shoe   FPT   Both   2-4

Plastic shoe with laces for lacing. Geometric-shaped figures must be matched to the correct slots in order to fill in the shoe.

Peg Grading Board   BSC   Both   2-5

Child must sort and grade thirty wooden pegs for size and color to fit into a board with thirty holes.

Pegity   PAR   Both   8+

The object is to get five pegs of one color in an uninterrupted row while blocking opponents.

The Chicken in the Eggs   PMC   Both   3-6

Six plastic eggs, graduated in size, are taken apart to find the chick.

Skaneateles Transportation Sets   PMC   Both   2-10

Wooden railroad sets—tracks, cars, et cetera.

New Tot Railroad   PMC   Both   2-9

Twenty-eight piece plastic railroad set for beginners. Child builds in many ways.

Painting   Many   Both   3+
  1. **Water colors with brush**
  2. **Dri-mark water colors**
  3. **Tempera**

NAME OF TOY	MANUFACTURER	INTEREST	
		Sex	*Age*

Creative Blocks FPT Both 1-4
Plastic blocks fit over wooden dowels.

Nuts and Bolts HCM Both 1½-3
Sturdy plastic threaded bolt serves as base on which to fit four large nuts.

Nuts and Bolts CCE Both 2-4
Nuts and bolts made of plastic must be matched for size and color.

Busy Board BSC Both 2-5
Wooden board with bolts, nuts, hinges, et cetera for children to experiment with.

Indian Beads PMC Both 2-4
Large beads for stringing. **Note:** Toys like stringing beads will be very frustrating if the necessary skills are not present.

Beads for Stringing MBC Both 2-6
Different shapes, sizes, and colors.

Hex SGH Both 4-8
Eighty hexagon printed cards are matched according to color and design to form flowers.

Wooden Puzzles VIC Both 4-7
Simple wooden puzzles of familiar scenes and several alphabet puzzles.

Nail-On Tiles SGH Both 4-6
Plastic tiles, nails, wooden hammer, and board are provided for creating pictures and designs. Illustration sheet included.

NAME OF TOY	MANUFACTURER	INTEREST	
		Sex	*Age*

Juvenile Jigsaw Puzzles   SIF   Both   3-6

Two puzzles per box—each puzzle contains six pieces which are made out of durable material.

Toddler Inlay Puzzles   SIF   Both   2-6

Wooden puzzles of familiar objects ranging from five to twenty pieces.

Puzzles   PMC   Both   2-8

1. **Primary Puzzles**—one to twelve pieces
2. **Intermediate Puzzles**—ten to nineteen pieces
3. **Advanced puzzles**—fifteen to twenty-seven pieces

Boy and Girl Jigsaw Puzzle   BSC   Both   3-5

Fourteen pieces of children's clothing can be combined in different ways to complete the wooden puzzles.

Fairy Tale and Mother
Goose Puzzles   SIF   Both   3-7

Wooden puzzles ranging from ten to twenty-five pieces.

Puzzles   WAC   Both   4-8

1. **Mother Goose**—twelve piece cardboard.
2. **Little Helper**—eighteen piece cardboard.
3. **Story Time**—thirty piece cardboard.

Design Tiles   SIF   Both   3-6

Large plastic honeycomb-shaped tiles can be fitted into brilliant designs. Six colored keysheets are included.

Magnetic Construction Set   BSC   Both   2-6

Horseshoe magnet, a number of disc and bar magnets, and various-shaped metal pieces for constructing objects.

NAME OF TOY	MANUFACTURER	INTEREST	
		Sex	*Age*

Fit-A-Square   CCE   Both   2-4

Teaches child colors and form association by providing him with sixteen cutout rubber discs into which forty-eight pieces in twelve different shapes fit.

Judgments and Readiness   CPT   Both   4-8

Colored rubber squares, circles, and triangles are composed of five or more concentric outlines which can be taken apart and fit together to make a solid figure.

Super Puzzle   SGH   Both   7+

Sixty silhouette puzzles to be solved using plastic shapes. Instruction book and solutions included.

Tinker Box   CHI   Both   2-4

Plastic tool box into which large screws, nuts, and bolts can be put with the aid of a plastic hammer, screwdriver, and wrench.

Bag of Blocks and Rods   HAL   Both   3-5

Wooden ⅞" building blocks in eleven different shapes; ½" diameter wooden rods are used to attach blocks.

Workbench   PMC   Both   3-5

A wooden bench with wooden nuts, bolts, screws, and nails which can be manipulated.

Landscape Peg Set   PMC   Both   2½-6

Child constructs landscapes with pegs and wooden shapes.

Play Chest   HCM   Both   3-5

Wooden chest complete with blackboard, pegboard, mallet, and pegs.

NAME OF TOY	MANUFACTURER	INTEREST	
		Sex	*Age*

Peg Desk PMC Both 3-8

Desk with attached seat. Top of desk is a blackboard. Chalk and eraser are supplied. Under the top is a pegboard. Pegs are supplied.

Musical Instruments Many Both 3+

1. Drums   5. Recorder
2. Whistle   6. Tonette
3. Bells   7. Maracas
4. Xylophone   8. Guitar

Note: Simple rhythm instruments may be very satisfying at a low skill level.

Notchies CPT Both 3-5

Large plastic blocks interlock in various positions to assist the child in building precarious forms.

Interslot MCI Both 4-8

Thirty-four wooden pieces in six different shapes can be fit together to create structures.

Lacing Boot CPT Both 3-5

Wooden boot and heavy shoe lace for lacing.

All By Himself—Book CPT Both 3-5

Cloth book with washable objects to teach child to dress himself—button, snap, tie, and zip.

Dolls Many Girls 3-12

Dress and undress dolls and encourage imaginary play.

Sewing Cards WAC Both 3-6

Six cards and yarn are provided to make outlines around familiar objects.

NAME OF TOY	MANUFACTURER	INTEREST	
		Sex	Age

Sewing Cards—Fluffy Yarns   MBC   Both   3-8
Cardboard cards with punched holes to be laced with yarn.

Junior Workshop   HAR   Both   3-5
Four plastic tools and nails to use with plastic lumber.

Mr. Builder's Home Workshop   HAR   Both   3-5
Ten plastic tools, nails, and lumber for construction.

Animal Lacing Cards   SGH   Girls   4-7
Twelve extra large animal pictures to sew with colored wool—no needle required.

Sewing Cards   FAR   Girls   4-7
Six sewing cards and yarn which can be made into two story books.

Rainbow Towers   SGH   Both   4-7
Game involving skills prerequisite for learning to count using colored bead towers.

Magnetic Board and Wooden Forms   MCI   Both   4-7
Wooden cutouts are pieced to form a variety of characters.

Electric Train Sets   Many   Boys   5+
This category covers a variety of electric trains.

Popkins   HCM   Both   2-4
Six different plastic heads pop together to make many characters.

Lots-A-Links   AMS   Both   3-5
Plastic multicolored snap-close links which can make chains, bracelets, et cetera.

| NAME OF TOY | MANUFACTURER | INTEREST | |
		Sex	*Age*

Wood Playmates   CPT   Both   4-6

Seven wood bodies, four heads, and a quantity of arms and legs go together to make people.

Mr. Potato Head   HCM   Both   5-8

Four plastic vegetable heads and sixty pieces for creating facial and body parts.

Marble Maze Assortment   HCM   Both   5-10

The game comes in three themes. Players must skillfully guide the marble through the obstacle course from start to finish.

Toy Mazes   MBC   Both   6+
1. **Skill-it Frying Pan**
2. **Fry-it Maze**
3. **Boob Tube**

Comic Corner   CCE   Both   3-5

Thirty-four interchangeable pegged parts to make your own street scenes. People, traffic light, and store parts are included.

Alphabet Inlay Puzzles   SIF   Both   3-7

Wooden puzzles ranging from fifteen to thirty pieces.

Fiberboard Inlay Puzzles   SIF   Both   3-8

Four puzzles per box. Each puzzle contains twenty to forty pieces—none are interchangeable.

Multi-Puzzle   SGH   Both   6-14

Forty-two plastic parts can be fit together into forty-eight different puzzles.

NAME OF TOY	MANUFACTURER	INTEREST Sex	Age

Museum Collage and
Construction Sets   CPT   Both   4+
  A collection of various materials (e.g. faille, cork, sponge, yarn,
  beads) for creating a collage.

Parquetry Blocks   MBC   Both   5-10
  Various-shaped wooden blocks fit together to make colorful
  designs. Design suggestions included.

Tinker Toys   Many   Both   3-8
  Assorted wooden Tinker Toy pieces and moving parts used for
  construction.

Standard Hammer-Nail Set   PMC   Both   3-6
  Twelve-inch square composition pounding board, laying sticks,
  nails, and hammer. Design sheet provided.

Construction Kit   MCI   Both   3-5
  Nuts, bolts, and connectors (wooden) are joined to form objects
  and toys.

Wood Toy Builder   PMC   Both   3-8
  Construction kit consists of wooden girders, nuts, bolts, screws,
  and appropriate plastic tools.

Action Soldier—G.I. Joe   HCM   Both   5-8
  Ten-inch male doll has numerous outfits for dressing; play
  equipment lends to action play.

Funblocks   SIF   Both   4-12
  Plastic interlocking blocks shaped like snowflakes. The set
  includes closed links, open links, corners, et cetera for endless
  combinations.

NAME OF TOY	MANUFACTURER	INTEREST	
		Sex	*Age*

Colorforms CCE Both 4-7
Make designs with die-cut plastic shapes which adhere to a plastic workboard.

Military Construction Sets HCM Boys 5-8
Interlocking plastic parts build bridges, observation towers, et cetera.

Greeting Cards BSC Girls 5-8
Gummed shapes to make greeting cards for all occasions.

Simple Things to Color PMC Both 4-7
Large pictures for young children to color.

Color-In Drawing Sets LAK Both 4-8
Lock-in-place drawing guides help children draw predetermined pictures which are colored by number.

Deluxe Magic Designer CPT Both 8+
Adjustable arms act as a guide for pen in creating and copying designs on circular sheets of paper.

Sketch-A-Bets SIF Both 4-7
Puzzles which teach numbers and letters. Child puts pegs into holes next to markings. Then he twists a white cord around the pegs following the proper order.

Magnetic Fish Pond SGH Both 4-8
The challenge of outdoor fishing at home. Ten plastic fish, four rods with magnets, and a colorful pond are provided.

NAME OF TOY	MANUFACTURER	INTEREST	
		Sex	Age

Children's Hour PAR Both 4-8

Three games in one; Peanut the Elephant, Porky Pig, and ABC Fishing. Child uses a miniature fishing pole to catch cardboard fish on a playing board.

Barrel of Monkeys LAK Both 4-8

The object is to use one plastic monkey to hook another from the barrel to form a long chain.

Giant Snap-Lock Ring and Beads FPT Both 2-4

Colored plastic parts snap together to make chains, et cetera.

Snap 'N' Play SIF Both 4-7

Wooden pieces of various shapes and sizes snap together to make objects.

Loony Links AMS Both 5-8

Snap parts of bodies together to form animals and people.

Tiddily Turtle AMS Both 5-10

Tiddly Winks in a new action game. The object is to snap winks into a turtle back and advance your turtle toward the finish line.

Tiddly Winks MCI Both 5-10
 FAR Both 5-10

Plastic winks are used to pop each other into the mushroom-shaped wooden target.

Jumbo Tiddledy Winks MBC Both 6-12

Child uses large winks to pop smaller winks into a cup in the center of the playing board.

NAME OF TOY	MANUFACTURER	INTEREST	
		Sex	*Age*

Flips   SGH   Both   6-12

Similar to Tiddly Winks. The plastic dots must be flipped into the target cup.

Bolts and Nuts Builder   KOH   Both   4-6

Large wooden and plastic bolts, nuts, wheels, and other parts can be combined to form movable toys.

Wooden Plane   MCI   Both   3-8

Forty-three wooden pieces including nuts, bolts, and connectors which can be used for construction of many objects.

Bolt-It   CPT   Both   4-8

Large wooden, plastic, and metal parts to make rolling and stationary toys from suggested designs.

Hardwood Construction Set   MCI   Both   3-7

Fifty building parts—nuts, bolts, screws, drilled strips, pulleys, and four rubber tires. Wooden wrench, screwdriver, and guide booklet provided.

Lincoln Logs   PMC   Both   4-8

                           HAL   Both   4-8

Three-quarter-inch hardwood logs and other material for construction of buildings.

Fun Time Clock   WAC   Both   4-7

Hands, gears, and other parts can be taken apart and put back together.

Take-Apart Truck and Kiddie Car   PMC   Both   4-6

Two over-sized vehicles which children take apart, put together, and ride. Has wooden nuts, bolts, a wrench, and a screwdriver.

NAME OF TOY	MANUFACTURER	INTEREST	
		Sex	*Age*

Hammer and Nail Set   CCE   Both   4-6

Set includes a board, hammer, object blocks, nails, and sticks to be used in creating pictures on a wallboard.

Hammer and Nail Set   HAL   Both   4-7

Pounding board 12" by 10". Colored heads of Huck, Yogi, et cetera in chipboard; laying sticks, nails, and hammer are used to create humorous scenes.

Picture Beads   HAL   Both   4-10

Small beads push into white Styrofoam to create pictures from a design sheet.

Hammer-Nail Design Board Set   CPT   Both   5-10

Two hundred varied die-cut steel shapes. Hammer and nails are used to construct designs on wallboards.

Balance Building Set   MCI   Both   5-10

Fifteen odd-shaped blocks for building towers.

Blockhead   CCE   Both   6+

Many different-shaped wooden blocks are placed one on top of another. The object is to add shapes without tumbling the structure.

Paper Dolls   MBC   Girls   5-12

For the young child, start with large dolls and uncomplicated clothes to be cut out.

Sew A Toy   MBC   Both   4-10

Chipboard is sewn together to make a wallet, jewelry box, et cetera. Materials are included for decorating them.

NAME OF TOY	MANUFACTURER	INTEREST Sex	Age

Make-It-Box   MBC   Both   4-10
  Variety of activities (e.g. make 3-D objects, mobiles). Stencils,
  crayons, and paints are supplied.

Spin 'N' Color   MBC   Both   4-9
  A competitive game to see colors. The first to finish wins.
  Twenty-seven pictures with wipe-off surface and crayons.

Make Your Own Action Puppets   MBC   Both   4-10
  Six puppet figures and materials used to assemble them including crayons.

Miniature Set-up Kits   MCI   Both   4-6
  Wooden cutouts can be put together to form multiple familiar
  scenes such as school rooms, farm, airport, et cetera.

Rubber Beaded Pegboards CPT   Both   4-8
  Duplicate or make designs with pegs on the board.

Krupferli   CPT   Both   4-8
  Plastic components for making chains, shapes, baskets, and
  geometric forms.

Kinder Suburbia   SIF   Both   4-8
  Block city in which child decides the number of stories, types
  of buildings, pitch of the roof, and location on imaginary
  streets.

Block City   CCE   Both   5-8
  These sets supply plastic interlocking blocks cut for building
  houses, stores, and buildings.

NAME OF TOY	MANUFACTURER	INTEREST	
		Sex	*Age*

American Plastic Bricks HAL Both 5-8

Interlocking plastic bricks can be used to create many different objects.

Lego System Blocks CCE Both 4-8

Interlocking blocks of different shapes and primary colors can be combined to form sturdy structures.

Bill Ding SIF Both 4-10

Wooden clowns can be manipulated to perform thousands of balancing acts on wooden rods.

Carom Jump Ball CAR Both 5-10

The object is to shoot all of your table tennis balls over the net onto your opponent's side by aiming and pulling the lever. The player with the least number of balls is the winner.

Shoot 'Em Down Soldier Set HAR Both 3-6

Ten plastic soldiers on a rack. The object is to shoot them down with corks ejected from toy cannons attached to a lever.

Pow! The Cannon Game MBC Both 5-12

Players fire at each others' standing army by pulling the lever of a cannon loaded with marbles.

Wow! Pillow Fight Game MBC Girls 5-12

Players attempt to knock down their opponents' men with plastic pillows ejected from miniature beds operated by a lever.

Frantic Frogs MBC Both 5-12

Players wind plastic frogs and race on a board. Each player must be quick to direct his frog with a stick into the correct cove. Requires quick reflex action.

NAME OF TOY	MANUFACTURER	INTEREST Sex	Age

Braiding   Many   Both   5-12
   Braid simple lanyards out of colored laces.

Magnasticks   CCE   Both   5-7
   Magnetic plates hold metal construction parts together while building structures.

Building Models   Many   Boys   6-14
   Precut plastic or wooden parts must be glued together following a pattern to make objects such as cars, boats, and planes. Note: Models exist at all levels of complexity. They should be carefully selected for suitability.

Pegboard Playtiles   HAL   Both   5-10
   A total of 448 plastic tiles in three different shapes fit snugly into pegboard to create mosaic designs and pictures.

Rig-A-Jig   CCE   Both   5-7
   Colorful plastic pieces interlock to form people, animals, trucks, and geometric forms.

Constructioneer   HAL   Both   5-8
   Interlocking plastic blocks in a multitude of different shapes are used to build complicated objects.

Asymmetric Space Construction   CPT   Both   4-8
   Sixty pieces of various-sized rods and dowels for construction of various objects.

Inventatoy   CPT   Both   4-8
   Dowels and connector parts can be manipulated to form toys with movable parts.

| NAME OF TOY | MANUFACTURER | INTEREST | |
| | | *Sex* | *Age* |

Snap-Eze Playforms — CCE — Both — 5-7

A collection of unbreakable plastic rods, wheels, and blocks all interlocking to build a wide range of objects (e.g. people, houses, cars).

Bend 'N' Build Construction Set — CCE — Both — 6-10

Big unbreakable plastic tubes for construction of large-scale models. Connectors link tubes, and parts are movable.

Flexagons — CCE — Both — 5-8

Four cardboard squares and triangles assemble with rubber bands to form 3-D boats, houses, and geometric forms.

Stencil Art—Book — AMS — Girls — 6-10

Child can trace designs onto paper, cloth for embroidering, et cetera.

Learn-to Write Letter Cards — MBC — Both — 6-8

Reusable cards on which the child traces printed letters with crayons. Manuscript and cursive letters are included.

Crayon Coloring Cards — SGH — Both — 5-8

Ten stencil cards showing colors to be used to teach the first steps in drawing. Crayons are supplied.

Color-A-Long Book — WAC — Both — 5-8

Forty-five inches of running pictures to color and recolor. Surface can be wiped off again and again.

Mary Poppins Paint and Crayon Set — HCM — Both — 5-8

Presketched pictures to paint or color, with painting hints included.

NAME OF TOY	MANUFACTURER	INTEREST	
		Sex	*Age*

Poster Stencil Set   FAR   Both   6-10
Cardboard stencils—1 to 1½" high capital and lowercase letters, numerals, et cetera.

Activity Travel Kit   MBC   Both   4-12
Includes games, puzzles, mazes, doodles, et cetera.

Activity Fun   WPC   Both   5-10
Soft-cover book of activities such as dot-to-dot completion of pictures, mazes, pictures to finish, and simple objects to make.

Tic-Tac-Toe Target Game   CAD   Both   5-10
The object is to shoot a plastic ball at pails on the inclined 3-D target by pulling a lever.

Flippo   AMS   Both   5-10
Marbles are flipped at targets in the center of the board by aiming a plastic basket attached to a lever.

Flying Hats   SGH   Both   6-14
Plastic hats are flipped at a target by pulling levers. Score varies with ability to hit certain areas on the target.

Shenanagins   MBC   Both   5-12
This is a real carnival—3-D game. Players move on a board and test their skill at miniature carnival games.

Sharp Shooter   CAD   Both   5-10
A target game. Players use a plastic pistol and rubber-band ammunition to shoot at mounted targets.

Shoot-Out   MBC   Both   5-12
Shoot at targets on small plastic board.

NAME OF TOY	MANUFACTURER	INTEREST	
		Sex	*Age*

Shootin Gallery Set   MTI   Boys   6-10

Includes toy Winchester and pistol, plastic bullets, caps, and target.

Zing-A-Ring   AMS   Both   5-8

Six plastic rings are shot from a spring action gun at a desired target.

Crazy Maze   LAK   Both   6-10

Players guide marbles past traps in the incline maze to the winner's gate by remote control.

Paddle-Pango   AMS   Both   5-10

A miniature table tennis game. Plastic balls are hit with small plastic paddles controlled by a lever.

Drag Strip   MBC   Both   5-12

Players propel race cars down drag strips with marbles.

Top Ten Pins   PAR   Both   6+

Miniature bowling. A spinning top knocks down small plastic pins.

Top Shuffleboard   PAR   Both   6+

A miniature shuffleboard game. Players use a spinning top to guide discs.

Nok-Hockey   CAR   Boys   6+

A miniature hockey game. Players hit wooden pucks with hockey sticks. The object is to get the puck into the opponent's goal. **Note:** With competitive games that require extensive fine-motor control, it is best to see that the child is not frustrated by being overmatched with a young child who is more normal in development.

NAME OF TOY	MANUFACTURER	INTEREST	
		Sex	*Age*

Bottlecap Baseball   AMS   **Boys**   **6-10**
Authentic plays on a 4' by 4' board, utilizing bottlecaps.

Kik-It   CAR   **Both**   **6+**
This is a soccer-hockey-basketball combination. A table tennis ball is advanced to opponent's basket by wire hoops attached to rods.

Glitter Color Kit   MBC   **Both**   **5-12**
Contains stencils and two types of paint—Glitter Tone and Silk Tone.

Paper Plays   CPT   **Both**   **8-12**
Patterned paper is folded and cut to form 3-D sculptures.

Leather Craft   Many   **Both**   **5-12**
Use precut patterns or cut your own; punch holes in it and lace together to make useful items such as billfolds and moccasins.

Leather Craft   RBI   **Both**   **8+**
Contains precut leather parts for lacing and decorating with paint. They can be made into key chain purses, billfolds, et cetera.

Flower Craft   BSC   **Girls**   **5-8**
Make your own floral arrangements. Flower parts are provided with complete instructions.

Sewing Machine Set   HCM   **Girls**   **5-8**
Sets include miniature machine that operates by hand; needles, thread, thimble, scissors, patterns, and material are furnished.

NAME OF TOY	MANUFACTURER	INTEREST	
		Sex	*Age*

Luggage Sewing Assortment HCM Girls 5-8

Three different sets—embroidery, sewing, and stitch-a-story. All necessary materials included.

Paint By Number HCM Both 5-8

Numbered pictures of television characters (e.g. Flipper, Bambi) and water colors.

Three-Dimensional Pencil By Number HCM Both 5-10

3-D pictures of familiar television characters and shows to be completed with pencil crayons.

Paint By Number Books WPC Both 6-10

Paint with water colors following number instructions.

Paint By Number—Oil Paints HCM Both 6-10

Presketched, numbered pictures of familiar television stars.

Table Mat Printing SGH Girls 6-10

Nine coasters printed with outline designs ready for painting. All necessary equipment supplied.

Table Mat Stencilling SGH Girls 8-14

Seven coasters on which water-resistant pictures are painted with the aid of stencils.

Playmates SGH Girls 7-10

Four precut animal shapes to be stitched together and stuffed. All necessary articles furnished.

Creating With Wood Many Boys 5+

Use tools and a pattern to make simple objects (e.g. go-carts, simple furniture).

NAME OF TOY	MANUFACTURER	INTEREST	
		Sex	Age

Constructo Straws   PAR   Both   6-10
> Two hundred flexible plastic straws can be joined to make large-scale models.

Woodcraft Parts, Senior Set   CPT   Boys   6-12
> An assortment of wooden handles, spools, wheels, and balls which can be combined in various ways with the aid of nails.

Geodestix Construction Kit   CPT   Both   6-12
> Sturdy rods and plastic connector joints can be manipulated to form interesting 3-D designs.

Electrical Invention Box   CPT   Boys   6-10
> Contains twenty-six pieces (light bulb, sockets, switches, bell, buzzer, etc.) which are operated by a harmless six-volt battery.

Electrical Invention Box   CPT   Boys   6-12
> Kit includes wire, bulbs, sockets, switches, buzzers, motors, et cetera. No instructions are included, to encourage the child to experiment.

Junior Electro-Experimental Set   RBI   Boys   10-16
> Child learns the principle of electricity by putting together simple, safe, everyday components.

Loom Craft   HCM   Girls   5-12
> Various-size looms and cotton loopers to weave to make pot holders, et cetera. Designs can be copied or created.

Basket Making   SGH   Girls   5-8
> Includes precut sticks and paper strips with instructions for making six baskets.

| NAME OF TOY | MANUFACTURER | INTEREST | |
| | | *Sex* | *Age* |

Flower Basket   SGH   Girls   6-10

A tray full of plastic flower parts to make floral decorations. Plastic baskets and weaving material are provided.

Weave-A-Basket   SGH   Girls   6-10

Five baskets can be made out of basic shapes and plastic strips.

Raffia Baskets   SGH   Girls   6-9

Includes four colored basket shapes and raffia for weaving.

Knitting Ring   SGH   Girls   6-10

Knit with the assistance of a frame. Practice wool and colored illustrations are supplied.

My Knitting Set   PAR   Girls   6-12

Learn to knit with the aid of a special tool.

Mary Poppins Giant Knitting Spool   HCM   Girls   6-10

Make many useful items from this kit. All necessary materials included as well as instruction book.

Knitting Nancy   SGH   Girls   8-10

Knit long strands with the aid of a wooden frame. These strands can be combined to make mats, rugs, et cetera.

Pompon Pets   SGH   Girls   8-12

Miniature pets can be made out of yarn with the help of forms. Comes with complete instructions and all necessary equipment.

Ceramic Tiles   Many   Both   8+

Decorate precut forms such as dishes and ash trays with tiles held together by grout.

NAME OF TOY	MANUFACTURER	INTEREST	
		Sex	*Age*

Plaquette-Mosaic Wall Hanging   GCC   Girls   8-14

Make picture wall hangings using precut mosaic shapes and glue.

Mat Weaving   SGH   Girls   8-14

Six mats can be made using a ring loom and raffia.

Jewelry Craft Assortment   HCM   Girls   7-10

Four different sets—charms and chains, snap-in beads, Indian beads, and stone bracelets—all for creating your own jewelry.

Fiesta Jewelled Applique Set   RBI   Girls   8-14

Six colored felt cutout appliques ready for mounting with colored nail heads. Includes instruction sheet with suggestions.

Operation   MBC   Both   6+

Pick-up cards determine the type of operation the player must make on a plastic man with removable plastic parts. The part must be removed carefully with a tweezer in order to score points.

Jack Straws   PAR   Both   6+

Played similar to pick-up-sticks. Players must pick up small plastic tools from a pile randomly dropped from the box.

Pick-Up-Sticks   AMS   Both   5+

The object is to flip sticks off a pile without disturbing other sticks.

Double Pick-Up-Sticks   PAR   Both   6+

Players attempt to remove individual wooden sticks from a pile without disturbing the others.

NAME OF TOY	MANUFACTURER	INTEREST	
		Sex	*Age*

Stardust   HCM   Both   8-15

Similar to painting by number, but stardust and feathers are used to fill in the numbered sections. The finished picture looks like velvet.

Sand Art Drawing Set   RBI   Both   10+

Contains twelve picture cards, colored sand, sand pen, and glue.

Hockey   CAD   Boys   8+

Mechanical levers control puck and goalies in a miniature hockey game.

Indoor Bas Bal   CAD   Boys   8+

A miniature action baseball game where players manipulate levers to pitch and hit balls.

Are You On The Ball?   MBC   Both   8+

The players must guide ten steel balls into a center hole by pulling action levers. A scoring slot records the players' skill.

Deluxe Pool Table   HAR   Both   5-8

Two miniature spring-action cues shoot plastic balls into the pockets of a miniature pool table.

Pee Wee Pool   HCM   Both   6-10

A swivel plunger allows you to direct your play. Marbles are shot into pockets for scores.

Basket   CAD   Boys   8+

Miniature basketball. Players operate levers which throw the ball at the basket.

NAME OF TOY	MANUFACTURER	INTEREST	
		Sex	*Age*

Bagatelle Pin Ball   HCM   Both   6-10

Comes in three themes. Two action levers keep ball in play as long as possible to attain the highest score.

Booby Trap   PAR   Both   8+

Players score by removing plastic counters from the board. One wrong move may trigger a spring that scatters the pieces and the players lose points.

Slot Cars   Many   Boys   6+

Miniature electric racing cars which can be controlled at a distance. Skill is required to keep them at maximum speed without leaving the track.

Labyrinth   MFC   Both   8+

The player guides a small steel ball through the maze by tilting the board at different angles.

Erector Set   GIL   Boys   8+

A variety of metal building components and an electric motor for building structures.

Ship in Bottle   CPT   Boys   8-12

Child must glue precut parts of a boat and place in bottle, which is then glued together.

Mary Poppins Needlepoint Set   HCM   Girls   6-10

Tapestry, yarn, and needle are supplied. Finished product can be framed.

My Pet Hankies   SGH   Girls   8-10

Four pastel-colored hankies with four pet appliques to be sewed on. Thread and needles supplied.

| NAME OF TOY | MANUFACTURER | INTEREST | |
| | | Sex | Age |

Woolly Pictures SGH Girls 8-12

Six framed pictures are to be stitched to make miniature tapestries. Needles, wool, and guide sheet are supplied.

My Hankies SGH Girls 8-12

Five colored hankies printed for cross-stitch embroidery. Yarn and frame are supplied.

Embroidery Set PAR Girls 5-8

Child decorates a prestamped doll bedspread and pillow set. All necessary material included.

Mat Embroidery SGH Girls 8-12

Four colored linen mats printed with easy-to-follow designs. Yarn and frame are supplied.

Indian Bead Craft WAL Both 8-14

Decorate belts, moccasins, and other precut leather objects with Indian beads. Involves stringing beads into a design.

Burn-Rite Woodburning Sets RBI Boys 10+

Wooden plaques, coasters, bookends, et cetera designed for woodburning.

Burn 'N' Stain RBI Boys 10+

Wooden plaques to be burned and stained by number.

Knot Tying Board CPT Boys 10+

Booklet, practice board, and rope to learn various methods of tying knots.

Copper and Metal Tooling Many Boys 10+

Using a design, hammer a pattern into metal plates, et cetera with various tools.

NAME OF TOY	MANUFACTURER	INTEREST	
		Sex	*Age*

Rap-A-Tap Metalcraft Set   RBI   Boys   10+
Six designed metal plaques and tapping tools for making bookends and pictures.

String Figures   CPT   Both   10+
An instruction booklet tells how to create 105 designs out of string.

Woodcraft Set   RBI   Boys   8-14
Six designed plywood plaques and tools for wood carving and wood painting.

Burn-Rite Leather Craft   RBI   Boys   10+
Precut leather parts and necessary equipment for tooling and burning decorations. Many useful objects to make.

Knitting   Many   Girls   10+
Knitting with various regulation-size needles, using different weight yarns and following a pattern.

Sewing   Many   Girls   10+
Sewing by hand or with the aid of a machine, using regular patterns and various types of materials.

Paint By Number   Many   Both   10+
Intricate pictures to oil paint by number.

Weaving Loom   SGH   Both   10+
Children can make scarves, mats, et cetera on miniature looms. Comes with instructions for designing articles.

Junior Clockmaker Kit   RBI   Boys   10+
Put a real cuckoo clock together and make it run.

NAME OF TOY	MANUFACTURER	INTEREST Sex	Age
Silk-Screen Set	**CPT**	**Girls**	**10+**

All necessary equipment and instructions are included for creating greeting cards, stationery, placemats, et cetera.

Lithography Kit	**CPT**	**Both**	**12+**

Materials are provided for children to learn how to print cards, pictures, et cetera.

Glass Blowing Set	**CPT**	**Both**	**16+**

All equipment included for blowing your own creations.

GROSS MOTOR

Gross-motor skills are of great importance throughout childhood in social relations between children, particularly boys. The awkward, uncoordinated child is frequently ridiculed by others and excluded from group play. The child who comes to see himself as inept physically may avoid activities, thereby obtaining little practice and falling relatively further behind his peers. This type of cycle can be prevented by the parent who provides extra opportunities for practice in situations that are relatively protected from further defeat. It is sometimes helpful to have a child pick a sport on which to concentrate that will gain him the esteem of his friends. The proper one will vary in different neighborhoods but includes the opportunity for extra training. Examples are table tennis, swimming, pool, billiards, or golf. A feeling of accomplishment in one sport will diminish the feelings of inadequacy related to lack of accomplishment in other areas.

If the child already feels inept, he is likely to do better with games that he can play with a parent as opposed to team games. Patience is a prime necessity when dealing with the child with gross-motor difficulties since there will be many frustrations and progress will be slow.

NAME OF TOY	MANUFACTURER	INTEREST	
		Sex	Age

Sandbox Play   Many   Both   2-5
Give the child different-sized bottles, cans, jars, funnels, pans, sieves for filling and dumping the sand.

Cobbler's Bench   PMC   Both   1-2½
Bang bench with movable wooden pegs. Child uses a wooden mallet for pounding.

Bowling Game   MBC   Both   4-10
Ten wooden soldiers to be bowled over by small wooden balls.

Toy Ironing Board and Iron   SIF   Girls   4-7
Girls can practice ironing their doll clothes.

Punching Bag On A Stand   Many   Boys   5+
Child punches at a bag.

Clown Bean Bag   PAR   Both   5-10
Child tosses bean bags into holes in a stand-up target.

Bean Bags and Board   Many   Both   5-10
Board with easel has five target holes of different sizes and shapes through which bean bags must be thrown.

Deluxe Horseshoe Set   HAR   Both   3-8
Four plastic horseshoes to be tossed at a peg target on a stand.

Ring Toss   MBC   Both   3-8
Wooden base target at which rope rings are tossed.

Ring Toss   HAR   Both   4-8
Four large plastic rings to be tossed at a target peg on a stand.

NAME OF TOY	MANUFACTURER	INTEREST	
		Sex	*Age*

Twister MBC Both 8+

Two players put all four extremities on colored circles on a plastic game rug. A spinner shows where the player must move his hands and feet next. This requires a sense of balance.

Hopscotch CPT Girls 5-12

A portable playing surface which can be used inside. One hops from square to square.

Bowling Set CPT Both 6-12

Eleven ½" unbreakable bowling pins and two large balls.

Bowl-A-Strike IICM Both 6+

Regulation size plastic pins and ball.

Suction Dart Game Many Both 4+

Games include targets and darts with suction cups.

Dart Game Many Both 4+

This game can be played with hand darts or dart gun. Child throws or shoots darts at a target.

Target Games Assortment HCM Both 5+

Three different metal targets and three rubber suction darts.

Toss-Up CAR Both 6+

The object is to flip a ring onto a hook attached to a rod, by springing another rod.

Hooper-Dooper AMS Both 6-10

A plastic hoop adaptable for scooting, bouncing, et cetera.

NAME OF TOY	MANUFACTURER	INTEREST	
		Sex	*Age*

Shuffleboard   **PAR**   **Both**   6+

Discs are propelled toward a target with a long implement.

Croquet   Many   **Both**   6+

Players propel a wooden ball through wire wickets with a wooden mallet.

Jump Rope   Many   **Girls**   6-10

A piece of rope with handles attached on each end. The object is to jump over the rope as it swirls in a circle.

Bat and Ball   Many   **Boys**   5+

Wooden or plastic bat and ball. The object is to hit the ball with the bat when someone throws it toward you.

Flying Hats   **HAR**   **Both**   5-10

Three flying hats can be tossed and caught between players.

Pitch Back   **CPT**   **Boys**   5+

This pitching device is a silent catcher which returns the ball to the player. A net attached to a steel frame with springs.

Stilts   Many   **Both**   5-10

Pair of poles fitted with a footrest somewhere along its length. Used for walking.

Wooden Hoops   **CCE**   **Both**   6-10

Various-size hoops are rolled and controlled by a stick.

Archery   Many   **Both**   8+

Using a bow, shoot arrows at a target.

NAME OF TOY	MANUFACTURER	INTEREST	
		Sex	*Age*

Skibble LAK Both 6+

Players race each other around the board with round discs (skibbles) which are played off the side boards.

Jacks Many Girls 8+

The player bounces a small ball and attempts to pick up varying numbers of jacks while catching the ball again.

Junior Pocket Billiards WAC Both 6+

Junior version of billiards. Includes ten balls, cues, and playing surface.

Magnatel MTI Both 6+

Ten games in one including Krokay and Bumper Pool.

Carom CAR Both 6+

The object is to shoot caroms into pockets on the board with a wooden cue stick.

Volleyball Many Both 8+

Using hands only, hit a ball back and forth over the net. Usually involves more than two players.

Basketball Many Both 8+

Involves dribbling and shooting the ball through a net basket attached to a wire loop elevated at prescribed height.

Shuttle Loop CPT Both 7+

Players hit a birdie through a metal hoop with wooden paddles.

Badminton Many Both 7+

Hit a birdie back and forth across a net with light-weight racket.

NAME OF TOY	MANUFACTURER	INTEREST	
		Sex	*Age*
Tennis	**Many**	**Both**	**7+**

Players hit a ball back and forth over a net with a racket.

Ping Pong	**PAR**	**Both**	**7+**

Players hit a plastic ball back and forth across a table net with a paddle.

Takrow	**SPO**	**Both**	**7+**

A plastic ball is caught in a basket attached to a short stick and thrown to the next player.

Jai-A-Lai	**Many**	**Boys**	**8+**

Using a wicker basket attached to a handle, toss and catch a small rubber ball.

Double Diabalo	**CPT**	**Both**	**9+**

Players must balance a rubber top along a string and work the string to increase the speed of the top. Top can also be thrown to the next player to catch on his string.

Juggling	**CPT**	**Both**	**10+**

Six rubber balls and step by step lessons on how to master this art.

VERBAL

Almost all of the games listed under any of the categories can be adapted to elicit and encourage verbalization from the child. This may be accomplished by asking the child specific questions, as well as by discussing both the concrete and abstract aspects of the toys and games with which he is playing. Of course, verbalization can also be encouraged in almost all daily activities by discussing the child's experiences at home, in school, and at play. A difficulty sometimes arises in relationship to the fact that an adult has a preferred rate of communication. The child with difficulty in verbal expression communicates slowly and at times an exchange is a painful experience requiring more patience than a parent can muster. The tendency, therefore, is for the parent to encourage and require only minimal speech from the child when a great deal of experience is needed.

The number of games that specifically require verbalization is not as great as would be imagined, and since so many games are adaptable, it appeared desirable to describe the development of speech in five broad stages. A few examples of specific games and toys that can be used to encourage spontaneous speech will be listed under each stage.

Words

There are stages of vocalization which precede the development of speech or the first word. The first words are nouns and simple verbs.

The parent can ask the child to name the objects as he points to them in a book or magazine or in the environment. Questions should be formulated in such a way that the child can respond with a one word answer (e.g. What is that? What is the boy holding?).

		INTEREST	
NAME OF TOY	MANUFACTURER	*Sex*	*Age*

Mini Pop-up Model Books   MCI   Both   1½-4

These books pop up in 3-D scenes of familiar settings (e.g. railroad station, airport).

Mini Pop-up Books   MCI   Both   1½-4

These books open up to show a 3-D illustrated story in full color.

Pairs—Word Game   MBC   Both   6-9

Contains three sets of cards to match: picture-picture, picture-word, word-word.

NAME OF TOY	MANUFACTURER	INTEREST	
		Sex	Age

Color Bingo   EUC   Both   5-8
Teaches color and number identification.

Picture Lotto Assortment   MBC   Both   5-12
    1. **Look and Learn**—pictures, letters, and words.
    2. **Geography**—shapes, sizes, capitals, products.
    3. **Animal**—animals, picture-word and word-word.
    4. **Word Building**—object-word, pronounce and spell.

Phrases

Vocalization phrases usually consist of two to four words (e.g. "Mommy go." "Boy fall down.").

The parents can ask questions and talk about pictures or events in daily living. Questions become more complicated and demand longer responses from the child (e.g. What do you see in that picture? What is the boy doing?).

Picture books and magazines are also good materials for teaching phrases.

Picture Lotto Assortment   MBC   Both   5-12
    1. **Look and Learn**—pictures, letters, and words.
    2. **Geography**—shapes, sizes, capitals, products.
    3. **Animals**—animals, picture-word, and word-word.
    4. **Word Building**—object-word, pronounce and spell.

Alphabet Picture Flash Cards   MBC   Both   5-7
Colored pictures of objects and alphabet letters. Games teach letter recognition and spelling.

Vowel-Links Poster Cards   MBC   Both   6-10
Cards have pictures and words with one or two missing letters. The child must insert the missing letters and pronounce the word.

NAME OF TOY	MANUFACTURER	INTEREST	
		Sex	*Age*

Beginning Consonant Poster Cards   MBC   Both   6-10

Cards have a picture and a word with one or two missing letters. The child must identify the missing letters and pronounce the word.

Phonetic Word Builder   MBC   Both   7-12

Build words, using individual cards with consonants, consonant blends, special blends, double vowels, and short and long vowel endings.

Arithmetic Quizmo   MBC   Both   7-12

Played similar to Lotto. Practice in addition, subtraction, multiplication, and division.

Incomplete Sentences

Three to five words, leaving out little word such as *and, the, is,* and *a* (e.g. "The Mommy going to town." "The boy running home."), comprise incomplete sentences.

The parents' request becomes more complex, requiring longer responses from the child (e.g. "Tell me about the picture." "Tell Daddy what we saw this morning.").

Picture books and magazines can be used effectively for this stage.

Complete Sentences

The length and complexity of sentences increases (e.g. "I am a big boy." "The girl and boy went to the zoo.").

The parents' communicative responses include complex questions and descriptive explanations. Parents can repeat the child's response and elaborate on what he has said using descriptive sentences. The abstract things in the picture which the child has not noticed can be brought to his attention (e.g. "Yes, that is a picture of a picnic. It looks like a warm, summer day and everyone is very happy.").

Discussing complicated pictures in books, talking about daily events, and reading to the child can help him learn to form complete sentences.

Logical Sequence of Sentences

A logical sequence must be learned to express ideas, feelings, experiences, and concepts (e.g. "Bobby hit John on the bus. He cried to his mother. Johnny always cries.").

The parents should read familiar children's stories such as *The Three Bears, Cinderella, Jack and the Beanstalk* and ask the child questions about them.

Story records accompanied by picture books, such as *Puss 'N' Boots* and *Jack and the Beanstalk,* are helpful.

Talk about daily events as they occur or have the child relate them to his daddy later.

Play Object Lotto and ask the child why things relate.

Sing songs or recite rhymes.

		INTEREST	
NAME OF TOY	MANUFACTURER	*Sex*	*Age*

Headstart With Music   CPT   Both   3-8

Two 12" LP records and an accompanying twenty-eight page book help to introduce children to listening and singing skills.

Junior Memory Game   CPT   Both   4-10

Child must remember location of matching cards. Cards may also be used as cues for story-telling.

Monopoly   PAR   Both   8+

This game deals with buying and selling real estate using paper money. Players attempt to bankrupt each other. **Note:** There are a number of other Monopoly-like games that serve a similar function. These are grouped together in the conceptualization category.

MANUFACTURER INDEX

Advanced Ideas Co.   AIC
  68A Broadway
  Arlington, Massachusetts
Amsco Industries, Inc.   AMS
  Hatboro, Pennsylvania
Brio Company**   MFC
  Sweden
  (Marshall Field & Company
  111 N. State St.
  Chicago, Illinois)
B. Shackman & Co.   BSC
  2 W. 35th St.
  New York, New York
Cadaco, Inc.   CAD
  310 W. Polk
  Chicago, Illinois
Carom Industries, Inc.   CAR
  1202 N. Rowe
  Ludington, Michigan
Childcraft Equipment Co.*   CCE
  155 E. 23rd St.
  New York, New York
Childhood Interests, Inc.   CHI
  Roselle Park, New Jersey
Creative Playthings, Inc.*   CPT
  Princeton, New Jersey
Ed-U-Cards Manufacturing Corp.   EUC
  36-46 33rd St.
  Long Island City, New York
Educational Fun Games   EFG
  P.O. Box 56
  Winnetka, Illinois

** This game is imported by Marshall Field & Company.
* Manufacturer as well as a distributor for other toy manufacturers.

173

E. E. Fairchild Corp.   FAR
   Box 3947
   Rochester, New York
Fortune Games   FOR
   1517 Levee St.
   Dallas 7, Texas
Fisher Price Toys, Inc.   FPT
   606 Grand Ave.
   East Aurora, New York
General Crafts Corp.   GCC
   3031 James St.
   Baltimore, Maryland
General Sportcraft Co.   SPO
   140 Woodbine St.
   Bergenfield, New Jersey
Gilbert Division   GIL
   Gabriel Industries, Inc.
   200 Fifth Ave.
   New York, New York
Halsam Products Company (Division of Playskool)   HAL
   3720 N. Kedzie
   Chicago, Illinois
H-G Toys   HAR
   (Harett-Gilmar Inc.)
   500 Ocean Ave.
   East Rockaway, New York
Hassenfeld Bros., Inc.   HCM
   1027 Newport Ave.
   Pawtucket, Rhode Island
Jotto Corp.   JOT
   28 E. 22nd St.
   New York, New York
Kalah Game Company   KAL
   27 Maple Ave.
   Holbrook, Massachusetts
Kohner Bros.   KOH
   P.O. Box 294
   East Paterson, New Jersey
Lakeside Toys   LAK
   Suite 1224, 200 Fifth Ave.
   New York, New York

Marlon Creations Inc. MCI
  29-04 37th Ave.
  Long Island City, New York
Mattel Toymakers MTI
  1424 Merchandise Mart
  Chicago, Illinois
Milton Bradley Company MBC
  74 Park St.
  Springfield, Massachusetts
Parker Bros. Inc. PAR
  90 Bridge St.
  Salem, Massachusetts
Platt & Munk Co. PMC
  200 5th Ave.
  New York, New York
Playskool Manf. Co. PMC
  3720 N. Kedzie
  Chicago, Illinois
Rapaport Brothers, Inc. RBI
  500 N. Spaulding
  Chicago, Illinois
Selchow & Richter Company SRC
  200 Fifth Ave.
  New York, New York
School House Industries, Inc. SHI
  170 Central
  Farmingdale, New York 11735
Sifo SIF
  834 N. 7th St.
  Minneapolis, Minnesota
Simplex*** SIM
  29-04 37th Ave.
  Long Island City, New York
Spears' Games and Handicraft*** SGH
  29-04 37th Ave.
  Long Island City, New York
Victory*** VIC
  29-04 37th Ave.
  Long Island City, New York

_____

*** These games are imported and distributed by Marlon Creations, Inc.

Walco Toy Co.   WAL
    38 W. 37th St.
    New York, New York
Whitman Publisher Co.   WPC
    1220 Maund St.
    Racine, Wisconsin
Winthrop-Atkins Co., Inc.   WAC
    Box 351
    Middleboro, Massachusetts
Young People's Records   YPR
    Sutton Distributors
    100 6th Ave.
    New York 13, New York

TOY INDEX

Expression				
Gross Motor	167			
Bagatelle Pin Ball		HCM	Both	6-10
Visual Perception				
Spatial Relations	78			
Expression				
Fine Motor	160			
Bag of Blocks		HAL	Both	2-5
Visual Perception				
Part-Whole	35			
Spatial Relations	61			
Conceptualization	107			
Expression				
Fine Motor	132			
Bag of Blocks and Rods		HAL	Both	3-5
Visual Perception				
Part-Whole	36			
Spatial Relations	64			
Expression				
Fine Motor	139			
Balance Building Set		MCI	Both	5-10
Visual Perception				
Part-Whole	39			
Spatial Relations	82			
Conceptualization	115			
Expression				
Fine Motor	147			
Bangaroo		AMS	Both	8+
Visual Perception				
Part-Whole	59			
Retention and Recall				
Visual Memory	100			
Conceptualization	129			
Barnyard Voices		MCI	Both	2-5
Visual Perception				
Like-Different	13			
Auditory Perception				
Like-Different	93			
Barrel of Monkeys		LAK	Both	4-8
Visual Perception				
Spatial Relations	67			
Expression				
Fine Motor	145			
Basket		CAD	Boys	8+
Visual Perception				
Spatial Relations	79			
Expression				
Fine Motor	159			
Basketball		Many	Both	8+

Expression			
Verbal	171		
Bend 'N' Build Construction Set		CCE	Both	6-10
Visual Perception			
Like-Different	29		
Part-Whole	54		
Spatial Relations	77		
Conceptualization	119		
Expression			
Fine Motor	151		
Bill Ding		SIF	Both	4-10
Visual Perception			
Spatial Relations	71		
Expression			
Fine Motor	149		
Bingo		SRC	Both	6+
		MBC	Both	6+
		FAR	Both	6+
Visual Perception			
Like-Different	23		
Auditory Perception			
Like-Different	94		
Block City		CCE	Both	5-8
Visual Perception			
Like-Different	28		
Part-Whole	53		
Spatial Relations	74		
Conceptualization	117		
Expression			
Fine Motor	148		
Blockhead		CCE	Both	6+
Visual Perception			
Spatial Relations	82		
Conceptualization	115		
Expression			
Fine Motor	147		
Blocks		PMC	Both	1½-8
Visual Perception			
Part-Whole	34		
Spatial Relations	61		
Conceptualization	106		
Expression			
Fine Motor	131		
Bolt-It		CPT	Both	4-8
Visual Perception			
Like-Different	26		
Part-Whole	50		
Spatial Relations	68		
Conceptualization	113		

Expression			
Fine Motor	150		
Broadside		MBC	Both	10+
Conceptualization	124		
Building Models		Many	Boys	6-14
Visual Perception			
Like-Different	29		
Part-Whole	54		
Spatial Relations	70		
Conceptualization	117		
Expression			
Fine Motor	150		
Burn 'N' Stain		RBI	Boys	10+
Visual Perception			
Part-Whole	52		
Figure-Ground	89		
Expression			
Fine Motor	161		
Burn-Rite Leather Craft		RBI	Boys	10+
Visual Perception			
Part-Whole	39		
Expression			
Fine Motor	162		
Burn-Rite Woodburning Sets		RBI	Boys	10+
Visual Perception			
Part-Whole	52		
Figure-Ground	89		
Expression			
Fine Motor	161		
Busy Board		BSC	Both	2-5
Visual Perception			
Spatial Relations	65		
Conceptualization	107		
Expression			
Fine Motor	137		
Camelot		PAR	Both	8+
Conceptualization	128		
Candy Land		MBC	Both	4-8
Visual Perception			
Like-Different	12		
Car Capers		SGH	Both	5+
Visual Perception			
Like-Different	19		
Part-Whole	43		
Careers		PAR	Both	10+
Conceptualization	125		
Carom		CAR	Both	6+
Visual Perception			

Copper and Metal Tooling		Many	Boys	10+
Visual Perception				
Figure-Ground	89			
Expression				
Fine Motor	161			
Coordination Board		SIF	Both	2-4
Visual Perception				
Like-Different	10			
Conceptualization	109			
Expression				
Fine Motor	135			
Counting Dominoes		CPT	Both	5-8
Visual Perception				
Like-Different	17			
Counting Frame		PMC	Both	3-8
Visual Perception				
Like-Different	14			
Conceptualization	110			
Crayon Coloring Cards		SGH	Both	5-8
Visual Perception				
Like-Different	12			
Part-Whole	43			
Figure-Ground	87			
Expression				
Fine Motor	151			
Crazy Maze		LAK	Both	6-10
Visual Perception				
Spatial Relations	79			
Expression				
Fine Motor	153			
Creating With Wood		Many	Boys	5+
Visual Perception				
Like-Different	29			
Part-Whole	47			
Spatial Relations	77			
Conceptualization	116			
Expression				
Fine Motor	155			
Creative Blocks		FPT	Both	1-4
Visual Perception				
Like-Different	10			
Part-Whole	34			
Spatial Relations	62			
Expression				
Fine Motor	137			
Croquet		Many	Both	6+
Visual Perception				
Spatial Relations	76			
Expression				

Conceptualization	121		
Dial Speller		HAR	Both	6-10
Visual Perception			
Like-Different	31		
Part-Whole	57		
Auditory Perception			
Like-Different	94		
Difference Puzzles		SIM	Both	3-6
Visual Perception			
Like-Different	14		
Conceptualization	110		
Expression			
Fine Motor	136		
Dig		PAR	Both	8+
Visual Perception			
Part-Whole	59		
Retention and Recall			
Visual Memory	101		
Conceptualization	129		
Dogfight		MBC	Both	10+
Conceptualization	124		
Dolls		Many	Girls	3-12
Visual Perception			
Part-Whole	44		
Conceptualization	108		
Expression			
Fine Motor	140		
Doodle Dialer		WAC	Both	4-10
Visual Perception			
Part-Whole	39		
Dominoes		HAL	Both	6+
		MBC	Both	6+
Visual Perception			
Like-Different	20		
Conceptualization	126		
Double Diabalo		CPT	Both	9+
Visual Perception			
Spatial Relations	84		
Expression			
Gross Motor	168		
Double Pick-Up-Sticks		PAR	Both	6+
Visual Perception			
Spatial Relations	80		
Figure-Ground	90		
Expression			
Fine Motor	158		
Drag Strip		MBC	Both	5-12
Visual Perception			
Spatial Relations	72		

Like-Different	30		
Figure-Ground	90		
Expression			
Fine Motor	161		
Erector Set		GIL	Boys	8+
Visual Perception			
Like-Different	30		
Part-Whole	56		
Spatial Relations	80		
Conceptualization	126		
Expression			
Fine Motor	160		
Facts-In-Five		AIC	Both	9+
Visual Perception			
Like-Different	33		
Part-Whole	60		
Retention and Recall			
Visual Memory	97		
Conceptualization	129		
Fairy Tale and Mother Goose Puzzles		SIF	Both	3-7
Visual Perception			
Part-Whole	42		
Expression			
Fine Motor	138		
Fiberboard Inlay Puzzles		SIF	Both	3-8
Visual Perception			
Part-Whole	44		
Expression			
Fine Motor	142		
Fiesta Jewelled Applique Set		RBI	Girls	8-14
Visual Perception			
Part-Whole	47		
Expression			
Fine Motor	158		
Fill 'N' Dump Bottle		CCE	Both	2-4
Visual Perception			
Spatial Relations	63		
Expression			
Fine Motor	134		
Finance		PAR	Both	8+
Conceptualization	125		
Fit-A-Square		CCE	Both	2-4
Visual Perception			
Like-Different	14		
Part-Whole	44		
Conceptualization	111		
Expression			
Fine Motor	139		

Form Boxes	PMC	Both	1½-5
Visual Perception			
Like-Different	10		
Conceptualization	106		
Expression			
Fine Motor	134		
Fortune	PAR	Both	4-10
Visual Perception			
Like-Different	11		
Frantic Frogs	MBC	Both	5-12
Visual Perception			
Spatial Relations	72		
Expression			
Fine Motor	149		
Funblocks	SIF	Both	4-12
Visual Perception			
Like-Different	21		
Part-Whole	50		
Spatial Relations	70		
Expression			
Fine Motor	143		
Fun Cards	PAR	Both	3-5
Visual Perception			
Like-Different	14		
Part-Whole	44		
Fun Time Clock	WAC	Both	4-7
Visual Perception			
Part-Whole	51		
Spatial Relations	68		
Conceptualization	116		
Expression			
Fine Motor	146		
Geodestix Construction Kit	CPT	Both	6-12
Visual Perception			
Like-Different	29		
Part-Whole	54		
Spatial Relations	77		
Conceptualization	119		
Expression			
Fine Motor	156		
Giant Rack-A-Stack	FPT	Both	1-3
Visual Perception			
Like-Different	9		
Part-Whole	34		
Spatial Relations	62		
Conceptualization	106		
Expression			
Fine Motor	134		

Visual Perception			
Part-Whole	47		
Expression			
Fine Motor	144		
Hammer and Nail Set		CCE	Both	4-6
Visual Perception			
Like-Different	21		
Part-Whole	45		
Conceptualization	113		
Expression			
Fine Motor	147		
Hammer and Nail Set		HAL	Both	4-7
Visual Perception			
Like-Different	21		
Part-Whole	45		
Conceptualization	112		
Expression			
Fine Motor	147		
Hammer-Nail Design Board Set		CPT	Both	5-10
Visual Perception			
Like-Different	22		
Part-Whole	49		
Conceptualization	112		
Expression			
Fine Motor	147		
Hardwood Construction Set		MCI	Both	3-7
Visual Perception			
Like-Different	26		
Part-Whole	50		
Spatial Relations	68		
Conceptualization	113		
Expression			
Fine Motor	146		
Headstart With Music		CPT	Both	3-8
Auditory Perception			
Like-Different	93		
Figure-Ground	95		
Expression			
Verbal	172		
Hex		SGH	Both	4-8
Visual Perception			
Like-Different	16		
Part-Whole	45		
Expression			
Fine Motor	137		
Hickety Pickety		PAR	Both	3-5
Visual Perception			
Like-Different	11		

Part-Whole	40		
Spatial Relations	64		
Conceptualization	115		
Expression			
Fine Motor	140		
Inventatoy		CPT	Both	4-8
Visual Perception			
Like-Different	28		
Part-Whole	50		
Spatial Relations	68		
Conceptualization	118		
Expression			
Fine Motor	150		
Jai-A-Lai		Many	Boys	8+
Visual Perception			
Spatial Relations	84		
Expression			
Gross Motor	168		
Jacks		Many	Girls	8+
Visual Perception			
Spatial Relations	81		
Expression			
Gross Motor	167		
Jack Straws		PAR	Both	6+
Visual Perception			
Spatial Relations	80		
Figure-Ground	90		
Expression			
Fine Motor	158		
Jeopardy		MBC	Both	10+
Conceptualization	129		
Jewelry Craft Assortment		HCM	Girls	7-10
Visual Perception			
Like-Different	28		
Part-Whole	49		
Expression			
Fine Motor	158		
Jolly Time Dominoes		MBC	Both	4-7
Visual Perception			
Like-Different	16		
Expression			
Fine Motor	133		
Jotto		JOT	Both	8+
Retention and Recall			
Visual Memory	101		
Conceptualization	130		
Judgments and Readiness		CPT	Both	4-8
Visual Perception			

Junior Pocket Billiards	WAC	Both	6+
Visual Perception			
Spatial Relations 82			
Expression			
Gross Motor 167			
Junior Workshop	HAR	Both	3-5
Visual Perception			
Spatial Relations 66			
Conceptualization 116			
Expression			
Fine Motor 141			
Juvenile Jigsaw Puzzles	SIF	Both	3-6
Visual Perception			
Part-Whole 38			
Expression			
Fine Motor 138			
Kalah	KAL	Both	6+
Visual Perception			
Part-Whole 57			
Conceptualization 120			
Key Kit—Arithmetic	SHI	Both	5-8
Visual Perception			
Like-Different 23			
Part-Whole 57			
Retention and Recall			
Visual Memory 99			
Conceptualization 121			
Key Kit—Arithmetic	SHI	Both	4-7
Visual Perception			
Like-Different 23			
Part-Whole 57			
Retention and Recall			
Visual Memory 99			
Conceptualization 121			
Key Kit—Spelling	SHI	Both	4-7
Visual Perception			
Like-Different 23			
Part-Whole 57			
Retention and Recall			
Visual Memory 99			
Conceptualization 121			
Key Kit—Spelling	SHI	Both	5-8
Visual Perception			
Like-Different 23			
Part-Whole 57			
Retention and Recall			
Visual Memory 99			
Conceptualization 121			

Labyrinth	MFC	Both	8+
Visual Perception			
Spatial Relations	79		
Expression			
Fine Motor	160		
Lacing Boot	CPT	Both	3-5
Visual Perception			
Spatial Relations	65		
Expression			
Fine Motor	140		
Lacing Shoe	FPT	Both	2-4
Conceptualization	106		
Expression			
Fine Motor	136		
Landscape Peg Set	PMC	Both	2½-6
Visual Perception			
Like-Different	16		
Part-Whole	37		
Spatial Relations	66		
Figure-Ground	86		
Conceptualization	112		
Expression			
Fine Motor	139		
Learn to Write Letter Cards	MBC	Both	6-10
Visual Perception			
Like-Different	54		
Retention and Recall			
Visual Memory	98		
Expression			
Fine Motor	151		
Leather Craft	Many	Both	5-12
Visual Perception			
Part-Whole	39		
Expression			
Fine Motor	154		
Leather Craft	RBI	Both	8+
Visual Perception			
Part-Whole	39		
Expression			
Fine Motor	154		
Lego System Blocks	CCE	Both	4-8
Visual Perception			
Like-Different	28		
Part-Whole	52		
Spatial Relations	74		
Conceptualization	117		
Expression			
Fine Motor	149		
Liddle Kiddle Games	MTI	Both	4-7

Like-Different	17		
Figure-Ground	87		
Conceptualization	114		
Lotto-Number		MBC	Both	7+
Visual Perception			
Like-Different	24		
Luggage Sewing Assortment		HCM	Girls	5-8
Visual Perception			
Like-Different	27		
Figure-Ground	89		
Expression			
Fine Motor	155		
Magnasticks		CCE	Both	5-7
Visual Perception			
Like-Different	22		
Part-Whole	53		
Spatial Relations	70		
Conceptualization	118		
Expression			
Fine Motor	150		
Magnatel		MTI	Both	6+
Visual Perception			
Spatial Relations	82		
Expression			
Gross Motor	167		
Magnetic Board and Wooden Forms		MCI	Both	4-7
Visual Perception			
Part-Whole	46		
Expression			
Fine Motor	141		
Magnetic Construction Set		BSC	Both	2-6
Visual Perception			
Part-Whole	40		
Spatial Relations	66		
Conceptualization	111		
Expression			
Fine Motor	138		
Magnetic Fish Pond		SGH	Both	4-8
Visual Perception			
Spatial Relations	67		
Expression			
Fine Motor	144		
Make-It-Box		MBC	Both	4-10
Visual Perception			
Part-Whole	44		
Spatial Relations	65		
Figure-Ground	89		
Conceptualization	109		

Like-Different	19			
Match Mates		CPT	Both	3-6
Visual Perception				
Like-Different	15			
Part-Whole	36			
Conceptualization	110			
Match-Ums		HAR	Both	5-8
Visual Perception				
Like-Different	31			
Mat Weaving		SGH	Girls	8-14
Visual Perception				
Part-Whole	48			
Spatial Relations	70			
Expression				
Fine Motor	158			
Memory Game		MBC	Both	10+
Visual Perception				
Like-Different	32			
Retention and Recall				
Visual Memory	97			
Military Construction Sets		HCM	Boys	5-8
Visual Perception				
Part-Whole	49			
Spatial Relations	70			
Conceptualization	118			
Expression				
Fine Motor	144			
Milles Bornes		PAR	Both	6+
Conceptualization	122			
Miniature Series		MCI	Both	1½-4
Visual Perception				
Part-Whole	34			
Spatial Relations	67			
Figure-Ground	85			
Auditory Perception				
Like-Different	93			
Conceptualization	109			
Miniature Set-up Kits		MCI	Both	4-6
Visual Perception				
Part-Whole	46			
Spatial Relations	67			
Figure-Ground	86			
Conceptualization	116			
Expression				
Fine Motor	148			
Mini Pop-up Books		MCI	Both	1½-4
Visual Perception				
Spatial Relations	64			
Figure-Ground	85			

Fine Motor	140		
Musical Toys		PMC	Both	1-3½
Auditory Perception			
Like-Different	92		
My Hankies		SGH	Girls	8-12
Visual Perception			
Figure-Ground	91		
Expression			
Fine Motor	161		
My Knitting Set		PAR	Girls	6-12
Visual Perception			
Spatial Relations	69		
Expression			
Fine Motor	157		
My Pet Hankies		SGH	Girls	8-10
Expression			
Fine Motor	160		
Nail-On Tiles		SGH	Both	4-6
Visual Perception			
Part-Whole	42		
Expression			
Fine Motor	137		
Nesting Blocks		MCI	Both	3-5
Visual Perception			
Spatial Relations	63		
Expression			
Fine Motor	133		
Nesting Toys		PMC	Both	1-3
Visual Perception			
Spatial Relations	63		
Conceptualization	106		
Expression			
Fine Motor	133		
New Tot Railroad		PMC	Both	2-9
Visual Perception			
Part-Whole	37		
Spatial Relations	65		
Conceptualization	111		
Expression			
Fine Motor	136		
Noah's Ark		Many	Both	4-6
Visual Perception			
Like-Different	14		
Nok-Hockey		CAR	Boys	6+
Visual Perception			
Spatial Relations	79		
Expression			
Fine Motor	153		

Visual Perception			
Spatial Relations	79		
Expression			
Fine Motor	153		
Paint By Number		HCM	Both	5-8
Visual Perception			
Like-Different	25		
Part-Whole	52		
Figure-Ground	87		
Expression			
Fine Motor	155		
Paint By Number		Many	Both	10+
Visual Perception			
Like-Different	25		
Part-Whole	55		
Figure-Ground	91		
Expression			
Fine Motor	162		
Paint By Number Books		WPC	Both	6-10
Visual Perception			
Like-Different	25		
Part-Whole	52		
Figure-Ground	90		
Expression			
Fine Motor	155		
Paint By Number—Oil Paints		HCM	Both	6-10
Visual Perception			
Like-Different	25		
Part-Whole	52		
Figure-Ground	90		
Expression			
Fine Motor	155		
Painting		Many	Both	3+
Visual Perception			
Figure-Ground	86		
Conceptualization	108		
Expression			
Fine Motor	136		
Pairs—Word Game		MBC	Both	6-9
Visual Perception			
Like-Different	23		
Retention and Recall			
Visual Memory	98		
Expression			
Verbal	169		
Panascopic Model Books		MCI	Both	1½-6
Visual Perception			
Spatial Relations	64		
Figure-Ground	85		

Conceptualization	112			
Expression				
Fine Motor	140			
Peg Grading Board		BSC	Both	2-5
Visual Perception				
Like-Different	14			
Conceptualization	110			
Expression				
Fine Motor	136			
Pegity		PAR	Both	8+
Visual Perception				
Spatial Relations	82			
Conceptualization	128			
Expression				
Fine Motor	136			
Peg Leveling Board		BSC	Both	2-5
Visual Perception				
Like-Different	14			
Conceptualization	110			
Expression				
Fine Motor	136			
Peg and Shape Sort Board		BSC	Both	2-5
Visual Perception				
Like-Different	10			
Conceptualization	110			
Expression				
Fine Motor	135			
Perquackey		LAK	Both	8+
Visual Perception				
Part-Whole	59			
Retention and Recall				
Visual Memory	101			
Conceptualization	130			
Pronetic Quizmo		MBC	Both	6-8
Visual Perception				
Like-Different	31			
Auditory Perception				
Like-Different	94			
Phonetic Word Builder		MBC	Both	7-12
Visual Perception				
Like-Different	32			
Auditory Perception				
Like-Different	95			
Retention and Recall				
Visual Memory	101			
Auditory Memory	104			
Conceptualization	123			
Expression				
Verbal	171			

See-Ques	CPT	Both	4-7
Visual Perception			
Part-Whole	51		
Conceptualization	115		
Selbright Chess For Juniors	SRC	Both	6-12
Conceptualization	128		
Sentence Builder	MBC	Both	6-10
Visual Perception			
Like-Different	31		
Part-Whole	58		
Retention and Recall			
Visual Memory	100		
Auditory Memory	104		
Conceptualization	123		
Seven Seas	CAD	Both	8+
Conceptualization	124		
Sew A Toy	MBC	Both	4-10
Visual Perception			
Part-Whole	38		
Expression			
Fine Motor	147		
Sewing	Many	Girls	10+
Visual Perception			
Like-Different	30		
Part-Whole	56		
Spatial Relations	80		
Conceptualization	127		
Expression			
Fine Motor	162		
Sewing Cards	FAR	Girls	4-7
Visual Perception			
Part-Whole	37		
Expression			
Fine Motor	141		
Sewing Cards	WAC	Both	3-6
Expression			
Fine Motor	140		
Sewing Cards—Fluffy Yarns	MBC	Both	3-8
Expression			
Fine Motor	141		
Sewing Machine Set	HCM	Girls	5-8
Visual Perception			
Like-Different	27		
Part-Whole	48		
Spatial Relations	77		
Conceptualization	119		
Expression			
Fine Motor	154		
Shapes, Colors, and Forms	CCE	Both	2-4

Expression				
Gross Motor	167			
Silk Screen Set		CPT	Girls	10+
Visual Perception				
Part-Whole	47			
Conceptualization	116			
Expression				
Fine Motor	163			
Simple Things To Color		PMC	Both	4-7
Visual Perception				
Part-Whole	38			
Figure-Ground	86			
Expression				
Fine Motor	144			
Skaneateles Transportation Sets		PMC	Both	2-10
Visual Perception				
Part-Whole	37			
Spatial Relations	65			
Conceptualization	111			
Expression				
Fine Motor	136			
Sketch-A-Bets		SIF	Both	4-7
Visual Perception				
Part-Whole	49			
Expression				
Fine Motor	144			
Skibble		LAK	Both	6+
Visual Perception				
Spatial Relations	82			
Expression				
Gross Motor	167			
Slate Bingo		WAC	Both	4-8
Visual Perception				
Like-Different	18			
Conceptualization	120			
Slot Cars		Many	Boys	6+
Visual Perception				
Spatial Relations	81			
Expression				
Fine Motor	160			
Smarty		EFG	Both	7-12
Visual Perception				
Like-Different	29			
Auditory Perception				
Like-Different	94			
Conceptualization	120			
Snap-Eze-Playforms		CCE	Both	5-7
Visual Perception				
Like-Different	29			

Stacking Toys	MCI	Both	2-4
Visual Perception			
Like-Different	14		
Part-Whole	37		
Spatial Relations	63		
Conceptualization	106		
Expression			
Fine Motor	135		
Standard Hammer-Nail Set	PMC	Both	3-6
Visual Perception			
Part-Whole	40		
Conceptualization	112		
Expression			
Fine Motor	143		
Stardust	HCM	Both	8-15
Visual Perception			
Like-Different	25		
Part-Whole	47		
Expression			
Fine Motor	159		
Stencil Art—Book	AMS	Girls	6-10
Visual Perception			
Like-Different	24		
Expression			
Fine Motor	151		
Stilts	Many	Both	5-10
Visual Perception			
Spatial Relations	76		
Expression			
Gross Motor	166		
Stratego	MBC	Both	10+
Conceptualization	128		
String Figures	CPT	Both	10+
Visual Perception			
Like-Different	33		
Part-Whole	55		
Spatial Relations	80		
Expression			
Fine Motor	162		
Suction Dart Game	Many	Both	4+
Visual Perception			
Spatial Relations	73		
Figure-Ground	87		
Expression			
Gross Motor	165		
Super Puzzle	SGH	Both	7+
Visual Perception			
Like-Different	29		
Part-Whole	45		

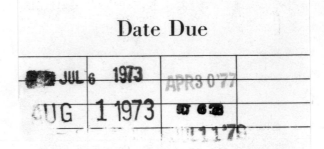